Junior Praise

Compiled by

Phil Burt, Peter Horrobin and Greg Leavers

COMBINED WORDS EDITION

Marshall Pickering
An Imprint of HarperCollinsPublishers

Marshall Pickering is an imprint of
HarperCollins*Religious*
Part of HarperCollins*Publishers*
77−85 Fulham Palace Road,
Hammersmith, London W6 8JB

First published in Great Britain in 1992 by
Marshall Pickering

Reprinted: 95 94 93 92
Impression number: 10 9 8 7 6 5 4 3 2 1

The compilers assert the moral right to
be identified as the compilers of this work

A catalogue record for this book is
available from the British Library

ISBN 0 551 02639-1 (Paperback)
      0 551 02638-3 (Cased)

There is no separate words edition for Junior Praise 2

Junior Praise Words Edition   ISBN 0 551 01366-4 (Single copy)
                                 ISBN 0 551 01292-7 (Pack of 25)
                                 ISBN 0 551 01572-1 (Easy-to-read)
Junior Praise Music Edition   ISBN 0 551 01293-5
Junior Praise 2 Music Edition   ISBN 0 551 02480-1

Printed and bound in Great Britain by
HarperCollinsManufacturing Glasgow

1

1. A boy gave to Jesus five loaves and two fish,
Not much you might say for a crowd;
But Jesus, He took them, and smiled at the lad,
Gave thanks to His father and blessed them out loud.

2. The boy then saw Jesus take loaves and the fish,
Not much for the folk on that day;
But Jesus, He broke them, and smiled at the lad,
Gave bits to disciples to then give away.

3. Then all worshipped Jesus as enough loaves and fish
Were given to every one there.
But Jesus just watched them, and smiled at the lad
Who'd given his lunch-box for Jesus to share.

2

Abba, Father, let me be
Yours and Yours alone.
May my will for ever be
Evermore Your own.

Never let my heart grow cold,
Never let me go.
Abba, Father, let me be
Yours and Yours alone.

3

Alleluia, alleluia, give thanks to the risen Lord!
Alleluia, alleluia, give praise to his name.

1. Jesus is Lord of all the earth.
He is the king of creation.
Alleluia, alleluia . . .

2. Spread the good news through all the earth,
Jesus has died and has risen.
Alleluia, alleluia . . .

3. We have been crucified with Christ—
Now we shall live forever.
Alleluia, alleluia . . .

4. God has proclaimed the just reward—
Life for all men, alleluia!
Alleluia, alleluia . . .

5. Come let us praise the living God,
Joyfully sing to our Saviour!
Alleluia, alleluia . . .

4

1. All people that on earth do dwell
Sing to the Lord with cheerful voice:
Serve Him with joy, His praises tell,
Come now before Him and rejoice!
Know that the Lord is God indeed,
He formed us all without our aid;
We are the flock He loves to feed,
The sheep who by His hand are made.

2. O enter then His gates with praise,
And in His courts His love proclaim;
Give thanks and bless Him all your days:
Let every toungue confess His name.
The Lord our mighty God is good,
His mercy is for ever sure;
His truth at all times firmly stood,
And shall from age to age endure.

3. All people that on earth do dwell
Sing to the Lord with cheerful voice:
Serve Him with joy, His praises tell,
Come now before Him and rejoice!
Praise God the Father, God the Son,
And God the Spirit evermore;
All praise to God the three-in-one,
Let heaven rejoice and earth adore!

5

1. All over the world the Spirit is moving,
All over the world as the prophet said it would be;
All over the world there's a mighty revelation
Of the glory of the Lord, as the waters cover the sea.

2. All over His church God's Spirit is moving,
All over His church as the prophet said it would be;
All over His church there's a mighty revelation
Of the glory of the Lord, as the waters cover the sea.

3. Right here in this place the Spirit is moving,
Right here in this place as the prophet said it would be;
Right here in this place there's a mighty revelation
Of the glory of the Lord, as the waters cover the sea.

6

Cecil F. Alexander 1818-1895

All things bright and beautiful,
All creatures great and small,
All things wise and wonderful,
The Lord God made them all.

1. Each little flower that opens,
   Each little bird that sings,
   He made their glowing colours,
   He made their tiny wings.
     All things bright . . .

2. The purple headed mountain,
   The river running by,
   The sunset, and the morning
   That brightens up the sky;
     All things bright . . .

3. The cold wind in the winter,
   The pleasant summer sun,
   The ripe fruits in the garden,
   He made them every one.
     All things bright . . .

4. He gave us eyes to see them,
   And lips that we might tell
   How great is God almighty,
   Who has made all things well.
     All things bright . . .

7

© 1986 Greg Leavers

All around me, Lord, I see Your goodness,
All creation sings Your praises,
All the world cries, 'God is love!'

8

John Newton 1725-1807

1. **Amazing grace! How sweet the sound**
   That saved a wretch like me.
   I once was lost, but now am found,
   Was blind, but now I see.

2. 'Twas grace that taught my heart to fear,
   And grace my fears relieved.
   How precious did that grace appear
   The hour I first believed.

3. Through many dangers, toils and snares,
   I have already come;
   'Tis grace has brought me safe thus far,
   And grace will lead me home.

4. When we've been there ten thousand
       years,
   Bright shining as the sun,
   We've no less days to sing God's praise
   Than when we've first begun.

9

W.C. Dix 1837-1898
Altered © 1986 Horrobin/Leavers

1. **As with gladness men of old**
   Did the guiding star behold;
   As with joy they hailed its light,
   Leading onward, beaming bright,
   So, most gracious God, may we
   Led by You forever be.

2. As with joyful steps they sped,
   Saviour, to Your lowly bed,
   There to bend the knee before
   You whom heaven and earth adore,
   So may we with one accord,
   Seek forgiveness from our Lord.

3. As they offered gifts most rare
   Gold and frankincense and myrrh
   So may we cleansed from our sin
   Lives of service now begin
   As in love our treasures bring,
   Christ, to You our heavenly King.

4. Holy Jesus, every day
   Keep us in the narrow way;
   And, when earthly things are past,
   Bring our ransomed souls at last
   Where they need no star to guide,
   Where no clouds Your glory hide.

5. In the heavenly country bright
   Need they no created light
   You its light, its joy its crown,
   You its sun which goes not down.
   There for ever may we sing
   Hallelujahs to our King.

10

J. Montgomery 1771-1854
© in this version Jubilate Hymns

1. **Angels from the realms of glory,**
   Wing your flight through all the earth;
   Heralds of creation's story,
   Now proclaim Messiah's birth!

   Come and worship,
   Christ, the new born King:
   Come and worship,
   Worship Christ the new-born King.

2. Shepherds in the fields abiding,
   Watching by your flocks at night,
   God with man is now residing:
   See, there shines the infant light!
     Come and worship . . .

3. Wise men, leave your contemplations!
   Brighter visions shine afar;
   Seek in him the hope of nations,
   You have seen his rising star:
     Come and worship . . .

4. Though an infant now we view him,
   He will share his Father's throne,
   Gather all the nations to him;
   Every knee shall then bow down:
   Come and worship . . .

11

Ask! Ask! Ask! and it shall be given you;
Seek! Seek! Seek! and you shall find;
Knock! Knock! Knock! it shall be opened
   unto you,
Your Heavenly Father is so kind.
He knows what is best for His children,
In body, soul, and mind;
So ask! Ask! Ask! Knock! Knock! Knock!
Seek and you shall find.

12
Attributed to Martin Luther 1483-1546
American translation 1884

1. **Away in a manger, no crib for a bed,**
   The little Lord Jesus laid down His sweet
      head.
   The stars in the bright sky looked down
      where He lay,
   The little Lord Jesus asleep in the hay.

2. The cattle are lowing, the Baby awakes,
   But little Lord Jesus, no crying He makes.
   I love You Lord Jesus! Look down from the
      sky,
   And stay by my side until morning is nigh.

3. Be near me, Lord Jesus; I ask You to stay
   Close by me for ever and love me, I pray.
   Bless all the dear children in Your tender
      care,
   And fit us for heaven to live with You there.

13
Caroline Noel 1817-1877
Altered © 1986 Horrobin/Leavers

1. **At the name of Jesus**
   Every knee shall bow,
   Every tongue confess Him
   King of glory now.
   'Tis the Father's pleasure
   We should call Him Lord,
   Who from the beginning
   Was the mighty Word:

2. Humbled for a season,
   To receive a name
   From the lips of sinners
   Unto whom He came,
   Faithfully He lived here
   Spotless to the last,
   Raised was He victorious,
   When from death He passed;

3. Lifted high triumphant
   Far above the world,
   Into heaven's glory
   Our ascended Lord;
   To the throne of Godhead,
   At the Father's side,
   There He reigns resplendent
   Who for man had died.

4. In your hearts enthrone Him;
   There let Him subdue
   All that is not holy,
   All that is not true:
   Crown Him as your captain
   In temptation's hour,
   Let His will enfold you
   In its light and power.

5. Brothers, this Lord Jesus
   Shall return again,
   With His Father's glory,
   With His angel-train;
   For all wreaths of empire
   Meet upon His brow,
   And our hearts confess Him
   King of glory now.

14

**Be bold, Be strong, for the Lord your God is
   with you,**
Be bold, Be strong, for the Lord your God is
   with you,
I am not afraid (No! No! No!)
I am not dismayed,
For I'm walking in faith and victory,
Come on and walk in faith and victory
For the Lord your God is with you.

15
Patricia Van Tine
© 1978 Maranatha/Word Music

**Behold, what manner of love the Father has
   given unto us,**
Behold, what manner of love the Father has
   given unto us,
That we should be called the sons of God,
That we should be called the sons of God.

16
Graham Kendrick
© 1985 Thankyou Music

1. **Big man standing by the blue waterside,**
   Mending nets by the blue sea.
   Along came Jesus, He said,
   'Simon Peter, won't you leave your nets
      and come follow me.'

*You don't need anything, I've got
  everything
But Peter, its gonna be a hard way.
You don't have to worry now, come on and
  hurry now,
I'll walk beside you every day.*

2. Life wasn't easy for the big fisherman,
   But still he followed till his dying day.
   Along came Jesus, He said,
   'Simon Peter, There's a place in heaven
       where you can stay.'
       You don't need anything, . . .

17

B. Gillman
© 1977 Thankyou Music

Bind us together Lord,
*Bind us together with cords that cannot be
  broken,
Bind us together Lord,
Bind us together, O bind us together with
  love.*

1. There is only one God,
   There is only one King,
   There is only one Body
   That is why we sing:
       Bind us together. . .

2. Made for the glory of God,
   Purchased by His precious Son.
   Born with the right to be clean,
   For Jesus the victory has won.
       Bind us together. . .

3. You are the family of God.
   You are the promise divine.
   You are God's chosen desire.
   You are the glorious new wine.
       Bind us together. . .

18

© 1986 Peter Horrobin

1. **Barabbas was a bad man,**
   Condemned to die was he,
   He'd done so many awful things,
   Was bad as bad could be.

2. But, Jesus was a good man
   God's only son was He.
   He did so many lovely things,
   The blind He made to see.

3. But Jesus some folk hated,
   They called "Put Him away".
   When Pilate made them choose the one
   To free that fatal day.

4. So Jesus though a good man
   Was killed on Calvary,
   But three days on He rose again
   To live eternally.

19

Anon
Copyright control

Bless the Lord, O my soul,
Bless the Lord, O my soul,
And all that is within me   } *Repeat*
Bless His holy name,

King of Kings (For ever and ever)
Lord of Lords (For ever and ever)
King of Kings (For ever and ever)
King of Kings and Lord of Lords.

Bless the Lord, O my soul,
Bless the Lord, O my soul,
And all that is within me   } *Repeat*
Bless His holy name.

20

Frances Van Alstyne 1820-1915

1. **Blessed assurance, Jesus is mine:**
   O what a foretaste of glory divine!
   Heir of salvation, purchase of God;
   Born of His Spirit, washed in His blood.

   *This is my story, this is my song,
   Praising my Saviour all the day long.*

2. Perfect submission, perfect delight,
   Visions of rapture burst on my sight;
   Angels descending, bring from above
   Echoes of mercy, whispers of love.
       This is my story . . .

3. Perfect submission, all is at rest,
   I in my Saviour am happy and blest;
   Watching and waiting, looking above,
   Filled with His goodness, lost in His love.
       This is my story . . .

21

© 1981 Roger Jones
National Christian Education Council

1. **Brothers and sisters,**
   In Jesus our Lord.
   Brothers and sisters,
   Believing His word!
   Now we're united,
   Made one in His love.
   We're brothers and sisters,
   In Jesus our Lord!

2. Jesus has saved us,
   From sin set us free.
   Always His people
   Together we'll be!
   This is the story
   We're telling the world!
   We're brothers and sisters,
   In Jesus our Lord!

3. Jesus has told us
   To be of good cheer,
   For He is with us,
   His Spirit is here!
   He gives us power,
   His message to share.
   We're brothers and sisters,
   In Jesus our Lord.

22

1. **Be still and know that I am God;**
   Be still and know that I am God;
   Be still and know that I am God.

2. I am the Lord that healeth you,
   I am the Lord that healeth you,
   I am the Lord that healeth you.

3. In You, O Lord, I put my trust,
   In You, O Lord, I put my trust,
   In You, O Lord, I put my trust.

23

By blue Galilee Jesus walked of old,
By blue Galilee wondrous things He told.
Saviour, still my Teacher be,
Showing wondrous things to me,
As of old by Galilee, blue Galilee.

24

1. **Children of Jerusalem**
   Sang the praise of Jesus' name:
   Children, too, of modern days,
   Join to sing the Saviour's praise.

   Hark! Hark! Hark! While children's voices
   *   sing*
   Hark! Hark! Hark! While children's voices
   *   sing*
   Loud hosannas, loud hosannas,
   Loud hosannas to our King.

2. We are taught to love the Lord,
   We are taught to read His word,
   We are taught the way to heaven:
   Praise for all to God be given.
   Hark! Hark! Hark! . . .

3. Parents, teachers, old and young,
   All unite to swell the song;
   Higher let God's praises rise
   As hosannas fill the skies.
   Hark! Hark! Hark! . . .

25

1. **Christ triumphant ever reigning,**
   Saviour, Master, King,
   Lord of heav'n, our lives sustaining,
   Hear us as we sing:

   Yours the glory and the crown,
   The high renown,
   The eternal name.

2. Word incarnate, truth revealing,
   Son of Man on earth!
   Power and majesty concealing
   By your humble birth:
   Yours the glory . . .

3. Suffering servant, scorned, ill-treated,
   Victim crucified!
   Death is through the cross defeated,
   Sinners justified:
   Yours the glory . . .

4. Priestly King, enthroned for ever
   High in heaven above!
   Sin and death and hell shall never
   Stifle hymns of love:
   Yours the glory . . .

5. So, our hearts and voices raising
   Through the ages long,
   Ceaselessly upon You gazing,
   This shall be our song:
   Yours the glory . . .

26

Clap your hands all you people,
Shout unto God with a voice of triumph.
Clap your hands all you people,
Shout unto God with a voice of praise!
Hosanna, Hosanna,
Shout unto God with a voice of triumph.
Praise Him, Praise Him,
Shout unto God with a voice of praise!

27

Cleanse me from my sin, Lord,
Put Your pow'r within, Lord,
Take me as I am, Lord,
And make me all Your own.
Keep me day by day, Lord,
In Your perfect way, Lord,
Make my heart Your palace,
And Your royal throne.

28

1. **Colours of day dawn into the mind,**
   The sun has come up, the night is behind.
   Go down in the city, into the street,
   And let's give the message to the people
       we meet.

   So light up the fire and let the flame burn,
   Open the door, let Jesus return.
   Take seeds of His Spirit, let the fruit grow,
   Tell the people of Jesus, let His love show.

2. Go through the park, on into the town;
   The sun still shines on, it never goes down.
   The light of the world is risen again;
   The people of darkness are needing our
       friend.
       So light up the fire . . .

3. Open your eyes, look into the sky,
   The darkness has come, the sun came to
       die.
   The evening draws on, the sun disappears,
   But Jesus is living, His Spirit is near.
       So light up the fire . . .

29

1. **Come let us sing of a wonderful love,**
   Faithful and true;
   Out of the heart of the Father above,
   Streaming to me and to you:
   Wonderful love
   Dwells in the heart of the Father above.

2. Jesus, the Saviour, this gospel to tell,
   Joyfully came,
   Came with the helpless and hopeless to
       dwell,
   Sharing their sorrow and shame;
   Seeking the lost,
   Saving, redeeming at measureless cost.

3. Jesus is seeking all lost people yet;
   Why can't they see?
   Turning to Him He forgives and forgets,
   Longing to set their hearts free.
   Wonderful love
   Dwells in the heart of the Father above.

4. Come fill my heart with Your wonderful
       love,
   Come and abide,
   Lifting my life till it rises above
   Envy and falsehood and pride;
   Seeking to live
   Life that is humble, with strength that You
       give.

30

Come listen to my tale,
Of Jonah and the whale,
Way down in the middle of the ocean,
Well, how did he get there?
Whatever did he wear?
Way down in the middle of the ocean.
A preaching he should be
At Nineveh you see
To disobey's a very foolish notion.
But God forgave His sin,
Salvation entered in,
Way down in the middle of the
Way down in the middle of the
Way down in the middle of the ocean.

31

Come on, let's get up and go,
Let everyone know.
We've got a reason to shout and to sing
'Cause Jesus loves us
And that's a wonderful thing.

Go! go! go! go! get up and go,
Don't be sleepy or slow.
You, you, you, you know what to do,
Give your life to Him.

Come on, let's get up and go,
Let everyone know.
We've got a reason to shout and to sing
'Cause Jesus loves us
And that's a wonderful thing.

32

1. **Come, you thankful people, come,**
   Raise the song of harvest home!
   Fruit and crops are gathered in
   Safe before the storms begin:
   God our maker will provide
   For our needs to be supplied;
   Come, with all His people, come,
   Raise the song of harvest home!

2. All the world is God's own field,
   Harvests for His praise to yield;
   Wheat and weeds together sown
   Here for joy or sorrow grown:
   First the blade and then the ear,
   Then the full corn shall appear—
   Lord of harvest, grant that we
   Wholesome grain and pure may be.

3. For the Lord our God shall come
   And shall bring His harvest home;
   He Himself on that great day,
   Worthless things shall take away,

Give His angels charge at last
In the fire the weeds to cast,
But the fruitful ears to store
In His care for evermore.

4. Even so, Lord, quickly come—
Bring Your final harvest home!
Gather all Your people in
Free from sorrow, free from sin,
There together purified,
Ever thankful at Your side—
Come, with all Your angels, come,
Bring that glorious harvest home!

33

Come to Jesus, "He's amazing"
People cried out when they saw,
People walking, who were crippled,
Blind eyes seeing, healed once more.

34

Come and praise the Lord our King,
  Hallelujah,
Come and praise the Lord our King,
  Hallelujah.

1. Christ was born in Bethlehem, Hallelujah,
Son of God and Son of Man, Hallelujah.
  Come and praise . . .

2. From Him love and wisdom came,
  Hallelujah;
All His life was free from blame, Hallelujah.
  Come and praise . . .

3. Jesus died at Calvary, Hallelujah,
Rose again triumphantly, Hallelujah.
  Come and praise . . .

4. He will cleanse us from our sin, Hallelujah,
If we live by faith in Him, Hallelujah.
  Come and praise . . .

5. He will be with us today, Hallelujah,
And forever with us stay, Hallelujah.
  Come and praise . . .

6. We will live with Him one day, Hallelujah,
And for ever with Him stay, Hallelujah:
  Come and praise . . .

35

Deep and wide, deep and wide,
There's a fountain flowing deep and wide;
Deep and wide, deep and wide,
There's a fountain flowing deep and wide.

36

Daniel was a man of prayer,
Daily he prayed three times.
Till one day they had him cast
In a den of lions.
In the den, in the den,
Fear could not alarm him.
God just shut the lions mouths
So they could not harm him.

37

1. Dear Lord and Father of mankind,
Forgive our foolish ways:
Reclothe us in our rightful mind;
In purer lives Your service find,
  In deeper reverence praise,
  In deeper reverence praise.

2. In simple trust like theirs who heard,
Beside the Syrian sea,
The gracious calling of the Lord —
Let us, like them, obey His word:
  'Rise up and follow me,
  Rise up and follow me!'

3. O sabbath rest by Galilee!
O calm of hills above,
When Jesus shared on bended knee
The silence of eternity
  Interpreted by love,
  Interpreted by love!

4. With that deep hush subduing all
Our words and works that drown
The tender whisper of Your call,
As noiseless let Your blessing fall
  As fell Your manna down,
  As fell Your manna down.

5. Drop Your still dews of quietness,
Till all our strivings cease;
Take from our souls the strain and stress,
And let our ordered lives confess
  The beauty of Your peace,
  The beauty of Your peace.

6. Breathe through the heats of our desire
Your coolness and Your balm;
Let sense be dumb, let flesh retire,
Speak through the earthquake, wind, and fire
  O still small voice of calm,
  O still small voice of calm!

38
G.R. Woodward 1859-1934

1. **Ding dong! Merrily on high**
   In heav'n the bells are ringing:
   Ding dong! Verily the sky
   Is riv'n with angels singing.
     Gloria, Hosanna in excelsis!
     Gloria, Hosanna in excelsis!

2. E'en so here below, below,
   Let steeple bells be swungen,
   And i-o, i-o, i-o,
   By priest and people sungen.
     Gloria, Hosanna in excelsis!
     Gloria, Hosanna in excelsis!

3. Pray you, dutifully prime
   Your matin chime, ye ringers;
   May you beautifully rime
   Your eve-time song, ye singers.
     Gloria, Hosanna in excelsis!
     Gloria, Hosanna in excelsis!

39
Karen Lafferty
© Maranatha Music/Word Music (UK)

Don't build your house on the sandy land,
Don't build it too near the shore.
Well, it might look kind of nice,
But you'll have to build it twice,
Oh, you'll have to build your house once
    more.
You better build your house upon a rock,
Make a good foundation on a solid spot.
Oh, the storms may come and go,
But the peace of God you will know.

Rock of ages cleft for me,
Let me hide myself in Thee.

40
E.H. Swinstead
Copyright control

Do you want a Pilot?
Signal then to Jesus;
Do you want a Pilot?
Bid Him come on board;
For He will safely guide,
Across the ocean wide,
Until you reach at last
The Heavenly Harbour.

41
Love Willis

1. **Father, hear the prayer we offer:**
   Not for ease that prayer shall be,
   But for strength that we may ever
   Live our lives courageously

2. Not for ever in green pastures
   Do we ask our way to be;
   But the steep and rugged pathway
   May we tread rejoicingly.

3. Not for ever by still waters
   Would we idly rest and stay;
   But would smite the living fountains
   From the rocks along our way.

4. Be our strength in hours of weakness,
   In our wanderings be our guide;
   Through endeavour, failure, danger,
   Father, always at our side.

42
J. Hewer
© 1975 Thankyou Music

1. **Father, I place into Your hands**
   The things that I can't do.
   Father, I place into Your hands
   The times that I've been through.
   Father, I place into Your hands
   The way that I should go,
   For I know I always can trust You.

2. Father, I place into Your hands
   My friends and family.
   Father, I place into Your hands
   The things that trouble me.
   Father, I place into Your hands
   The person I would be,
   For I know I always can trust You.

3. Father, we love to seek Your face,
   We love to hear Your voice
   Father, we love to sing Your praise,
   And in your name rejoice.
   Father, we love to walk with You
   And in your presence rest,
   For we know we always can trust You.

4. Father, I want to be with You
   And do the things you do
   Father, I want to speak the words
   That You are speaking too.
   Father, I want to love the ones
   That You will draw to You,
   For I know that I am one with You.

43
J.P. Hopps 1834-1911
Altered © 1986 Horrobin/Leavers

1. **Father, lead me day by day**
   Ever in Your own good way;
   Teach me to be pure and true.
   Show me what I ought to do.

2. When in danger, make me brave;
   Make me know that You can save.
   Keep me safe by Your dear side;
   Let me in Your love abide.

3. When I'm tempted to do wrong,
   Make me steadfast, wise and strong;
   And when all alone I stand,
   Shield me with Your mighty hand.

4. When my work seems hard and dry,
   May I never cease to try;
   Help me patiently to bear
   Pain and hardship, toil and care.

5. May I do the good I know,
   Be Your loving child below,
   Then at last in heaven share
   Life with You that's free from care.

44

Terrye Coelho
© 1972 Maranatha Music/Word Music (UK)

1. **Father, we adore You,**
   Lay our lives before You:
   How we love You!

2. Jesus, we adore You,
   Lay our lives before You:
   How we love You!

3. Spirit, we adore You,
   Lay our lives before You:
   How we love You!

45

Donna Adkins
© 1976, 1981 Maranatha Music/Word Music (UK)

1. **Father we love You,**
   We worship and adore You,
   Glorify Your name in all the earth.
   Glorify Your name,
   Glorify Your name,
   Glorify Your name in all the earth.

2. Jesus, we love You,
   We worship and adore You,
   Glorify Your name in all the earth.
   Glorify Your name,
   Glorify Your name,
   Glorify Your name in all the earth.

3. Spirit, we love You,
   We worship and adore You,
   Glorify Your name in all the earth.
   Glorify Your name,
   Glorify Your name,
   Glorify Your name in all the earth.

46

© 1986 Greg Leavers

'Follow me' says Jesus,
'I can keep you safe.
I am the Good Shepherd,
So why not be my sheep.
If you're lost and lonely
I can keep you safe,
I gave my life to save you,
So come, just follow me.'

47

D. Richards
© 1977 Thankyou Music

For I'm building a people of power
And I'm making a people of praise,
That will move thro' this land by My Spirit,
And will glorify my precious Name.

Build Your Church, Lord,
Make us strong, Lord,
Join our hearts, Lord, through Your Son,
Make us one, Lord, in Your Body,
In the Kingdom of Your Son.

48

Folliott Pierpoint
Altered © 1986 Horrobin/Leavers

1. **For the beauty of the earth,**
   For the beauty of the skies,
   For the love which from our birth
   Over and around us lies,
   Father unto You we raise
   This our sacrifice of praise.

2. For the beauty of each hour
   Of the day and of the night,
   Hill and vale and tree and flower,
   Sun and moon and stars of light,
   Father, unto You we raise
   This our sacrifice of praise.

3. For the joy of love from God,
   That we share on earth below.
   For our friends and family
   And the love that they can show,
   Father, unto You we raise
   This our sacrifice of praise.

4. For each perfect gift divine
   To our race so freely given,
   Thank You Lord that they are mine,
   Here on earth as gifts from heaven.
   Father, unto You we raise
   This our sacrifice of praise.

49

© 1976 Paul Deming

From the rising of the sun
To the going down of the same ⎫
The Lord's name   ⎬ *Repeat*
Is to be praised.   ⎭

Praise ye the Lord,
Praise Him O ye servants of the Lord,
Praise the name of the Lord,
Blessed be the name of the Lord
From this time forth,
And for evermore.

50

1. **Give me oil in my lamp, keep me burning.**
   Give me oil in my lamp, I pray.
   Give me oil in my lamp, keep me burning,
   Keep me burning till the break of day.

   Sing hosanna, sing hosanna,
   Sing hosanna to the King of Kings!
   Sing hosanna, sing hosanna,
   Sing hosanna, to the King !

2. Give me joy in my heart, keep me singing.
   Give me joy in my heart, I pray.
   Give me joy in my heart, keep me singing,
   Keep me singing till the break of day.
      Sing hosanna . . .

3. Give me love in my heart, keep me
         serving.
   Give me love in my heart, I pray.
   Give me love in my heart, keep me
         serving,
   Keep me serving till the break of day.
      Sing hosanna . . .

4. Give me peace in my heart, keep me
         resting.
   Give me peace in my heart, I pray.
   Give me peace in my heart, keep me
         resting,
   Keep me resting till the break of day.
      Sing hosanna . . .

51 © 1986 Greg Leavers

Glory to God in the highest,
Peace upon the earth.
Jesus Christ has come to earth,
That's why we sing, Jesus the King,
Jesus has come for you.

1. The shepherds who were sitting there
   Were suddenly filled with fear,
   The dark night was filled with light
   Angels singing everywhere.
      Glory to God in . . .

2. The next time we hear a song
   Of worship from a heavenly throng,
   Will be when Jesus comes again,
   Then with triumph we'll all sing,
      Glory to God in . . .

52 T. Ken 1637-1710
© in this version Jubilate Hymns

1. **Glory to You, my God, this night**
   For all the blessings of the light;
   Keep me, O keep me, King of kings,
   Beneath your own almighty wings.

2. Forgive me, Lord, through Your dear Son,
   The wrong that I this day have done,
   That peace with God and man may be,
   Before I sleep, restored to me.

3. Teach me to live, that I may dread
   The grave as little as my bed;
   Teach me to die, that so I may
   Rise glorious at the awesome day.

4. O may my soul on you repose
   And restful sleep my eyelids close;
   Sleep that shall me more vigorous make
   To serve my God when I awake.

5. If in the night I sleepless lie,
   My mind with peaceful thoughts supply;
   Let no dark dreams disturb my rest,
   No powers of evil me molest.

6. Praise God from whom all blessings flow
   In heaven above and earth below;
   One God, three persons, we adore
   To Him be praise for evermore!

53 Copyright control

1. **God is so good,**
   God is so good,
   God is so good,
   He's so good to me.

2. He took my sin,
   He took my sin,
   He took my sin,
   He's so good to me.

3. Now I am free,
   Now I am free,
   Now I am free,
   He's so good to me.

4. God is so good,
   He took my sin,
   Now I am free,
   He's so good to me.

54 Carol Owens
© 1972 Lexicon Music/United Nations Music
Publishing/Boosey & Hawkes Ltd

1. **God forgave my sin in Jesus' name.**
   I've been born again in Jesus' name.
   And in Jesus' name I come to you
   To share his love as He told me to.

   He said, 'Freely,
   Freely you have received;
   Freely, freely give.
   Go in my name and because you believe,
   Others will know that I live.'

2. All pow'r is giv'n in Jesus name.
In earth and heav'n in Jesus' name.
And in Jesus' name I come to you
To share his pow'r as He told me to.
    He said, . . .

55 Graham Kendrick
© 1985 Thankyou Music

God is good, we sing and shout it,
God is good, we celebrate.
God is good, no more we doubt it,
God is good, we know it's true.
And when I think of His love for me,
My heart fills with praise and I feel like
    dancing.
For in His heart there is room for me
And I run with arms opened wide.

56 © Chris Porteous / Jubilee Hymns

1. **God is our guide, our light and our**
   deliverer,
   He holds our hand, He walks beside the
       way.
   Lord, may our feet tread in the steps You
       taught us
   To follow firmly as by faith each day,
   Your word a light, a lamp to lead our
       footsteps
   We love the hours when You beside us stay.

2. God is our peace, our help and our
       protector,
   We find His presence in the hour of need.
   Lord, though the storms of life may leave
       us trembling
   Your words of comfort bring us peace
       within.
   When we are weak and fear to face the
       future
   We find such comfort in Your loving arms.

3. God is our hope, our joy and our salvation,
   His love alone transforms the sinful heart.
   Lord how we sought Your Spirit's sweet
       renewing
   Your healing touch has filled our hearts
       with praise.
   We come and worship Jesus, Lord and
       Saviour,
   His love alone must fill our earthly days.

4. God is our strength, our rock and our
       redeemer
   In times of trouble and in times of joy.
   Lord, may our lives be full of sure
       thanksgiving
   Our lips be full of symphonies of praise.
   You gave us love, a risen, living Saviour,
   We bring ourselves a sacrifice of praise.

57 A. Ainger 1841-1919
© in this version Jubilee Hymns

1. **God is working His purpose out,**
   As year succeeds to year:
   God is working His purpose out,
   And the time is drawing near:
   Nearer and nearer draws the time,
   The time that shall surely be,
   When the earth shall be filled
   With the glory of God,
   As the waters cover the sea.

2. From utmost east to utmost west
   Wherever man has trod,
   By the mouth of many messengers
   Rings out the voice of God:
   Listen to me you continents,
   You islands look to me,
   That the earth may be filled
   With the glory of God,
   As the waters cover the sea.

3. We shall march in the strength of God,
   With the banner of Christ unfurled,
   That the light of the glorious gospel of truth
   May shine throughout the world;
   We shall fight with sorrow and sin
   To set their captives free,
   That the earth may be filled
   With the glory of God,
   As the waters cover the sea.

4. All we can do is nothing worth
   unless God blesses the deed;
   vainly we hope for the harvest tide
   Till God gives life to the seed:
   Nearer and nearer draws the time,
   The time that shall surely be,
   When the earth shall be filled
   With the glory of God,
   As the waters cover the sea.

58 Gloria & William J Gaither
© 1971 United Nations Music Publishing/Boosey &
Hawkes Ltd

1. **God sent His Son, they call Him Jesus;**
   He came to love, heal, and forgive;
   He lived and died to buy my pardon,
   An empty grave is there to prove my
       Saviour lives.

   Because He lives I can face tomorrow;
   Because He lives all fear is gone;
   Because I know, I know He holds the future,
   And life is worth the living just because He
       lives.

2. How sweet to hold a new-born baby,
   And feel the pride, and joy he gives;
   But greater still the calm assurance,
   This child can face uncertain days because
       He lives.
       Because He lives . . .

3. And then one day I'll cross the river;
   I'll fight life's final war with pain;
   And then as death gives way to vict'ry,
   I'll see the lights of glory and I'll know He
       lives.
       Because He lives . . .

59

1. **God so loved the world He sent to us Jesus,**
   God so loved the world He sent His Son.
   Alleluia Jesus, Lord Jesus, Jesus;
   Alleluia Jesus, God sent His Son.

2. Jesus showed the world the love of the
       Father,
   Jesus showed the world how we must love.
   Alleluia Jesus, Lord Jesus, Jesus;
   Alleluia Jesus, God sent His Son.

60

God's not dead, (No)
He is alive.
God's not dead, (No)
He is alive.
God's not dead, (No) He is alive,
Serve Him with my hands,
Follow with my feet,
Love Him in my heart,
Know Him in my life;
For He's alive in me.

61

1. **God, whose farm is all creation,**
   Take the gratitude we give;
   Take the finest of our harvest,
   Crops we grow that men may live.

2. Take our ploughing, seeding, reaping,
   Hopes and fears of sun and rain,
   All our thinking, planning, waiting,
   Ripened in this fruit and grain.

3. All our labour, all our watching,
   All our calendar of care,
   In these crops of Your creation,
   Take, O God; they are our prayer.

62

1. **God whose Son was once a man on earth**
   Gave His life that men may live.
   Risen, our ascended Lord
   Fulfilled His promised word.

When the Spirit came, the church was born,
God's people shared in a bright new dawn.
They healed the sick,
They taught God's word,
They sought the lost,
They obeyed the Lord.
And it's all because the Spirit came
That the world will never be the same,
Because the Spirit came.

2. God whose power fell on the early church,
   Sent to earth from heav'n above.
   Spirit led, by Him ordained
   They showed the world God's love.

When the Spirit came, the church was born,
God's people shared in a bright new dawn.
They healed the sick,
They taught God's word,
They sought the lost,
They obeyed the Lord.
And it's all because the Spirit came
That the world will never be the same,
Because the Spirit came.

3. Pour Your Spirit on the church today,
   That Your life through me may flow.
   Spirit filled, I'll serve Your Name
   And live the truth I know.

When the Spirit comes, new life is born,
God's people share in a bright new dawn.
We'll heal the sick,
We'll teach God's word,
We'll seek the lost,
We'll obey the Lord.
And it's all because the Spirit came
That the world will never be the same,
Because the Spirit came.

63

1. **God who made the earth,**
   The air, the sky, the sea,
   Who gave the light its birth,
   Will care for me.

2. God who made the grass,
   The flower, the fruit, the tree,
   The day and night to pass,
   Will care for me.

3. God who, made the sun,
   The moon, the stars, is He
   Who when life's clouds come on,
   Will care for me.

4. God who sent His Son
   To die on calvary,
   He, if I lean on Him,
   Will care for me.

5. God who gave me life,
   His servant here to be,
   Has promised in His word
   To care for me.

64

1. **Great is Your faithfulness, O God my
   Father,**
   You have fulfilled all Your promise to me;
   You never fail and Your love is unchanging
   All You have been You for ever will be.

   Great is Your faithfulness,
   Great is Your faithfulness,
   Morning by morning new mercies I see;
   All I have needed Your hand has provided
   Great is Your faithfulness, Father, to me.

2. Summer and winter, and springtime and
   harvest,
   Sun, moon and stars in their courses above
   Join with all nature in eloquent witness
   To Your great faithfulness, mercy and love.
   Great is Your faithfulness . . .

3. Pardon for sin, and a peace everlasting,
   Your living presence to cheer and to guide;
   Strength for today, and bright hope for
   tomorrow,
   These are the blessings Your love will
   provide.
   Great is Your faithfulness . . .

65

Go, tell it on the mountain,
Over the hills and ev'rywhere;
Go, tell it on the mountain
That Jesus is His name.

1. He possessed no riches, no home to lay His
   head;
   He saw the needs of others and cared for
   them instead.
   Go, tell it . . .

2. He reached out and touched them, the
   blind, the deaf, the lame;
   He spoke and listened gladly to anyone
   who came.
   Go, tell it . . .

3. Some turned away in anger, with hatred in
   the eye;
   They tried Him and condemned Him, then
   led Him out to die.
   Go, tell it . . .

4. "Father, now forgive them" — those were
   the words He said;
   In three more days He was alive and risen
   from the dead.
   Go, tell it . . .

5. He still comes to people, His life moves
   through the lands;
   He uses us for speaking, He touches with
   our hands.
   Go, tell it . . .

66

**Hallelujah, for the Lord our God the
Almighty reigns.**
Hallelujah, for the Lord our God the
Almighty reigns.
Let us rejoice and be glad
And give the Glory unto Him.
Hallelujah, for the Lord our God the
Almighty reigns.

67

Hallelu, hallelu, hallelu, hallelujah;
We'll praise the Lord!
Hallelu, hallelu, hallelu, hallelujah;
We'll praise the Lord!
We'll praise the Lord, hallelujah!
We'll praise the Lord, hallelujah!
We'll praise the Lord, hallelujah!
We'll praise the Lord!

68

1. **Hark, the glad sound! the Saviour comes,**
   The Saviour promised long;
   Let ev'ry heart prepare a throne,
   And ev'ry voice a song.

2. He comes, the pris'ners to release
   In Satan's bondage held;
   The chains of sin before Him break,
   The iron fetters yield.

3. He comes the broken heart to bind,
   The wounded soul to cure;
   And with the treasures of His grace
   To enrich the humble poor.

4. Our glad hosannas, Prince of Peace,
   Your welcome shall proclaim;
   And heaven's eternal arches ring
   With Your belovèd name.

69

Charles Wesley 1707-1788
George Whitfield 1714-1770
Martin Madan 1726-1790 and others

1. **Hark! The herald-angels sing,**
   "Glory to the new-born King!
   Peace on earth, and mercy mild,
   God and sinners reconciled."
   Joyful, all you nations, rise,
   Join the triumph of the skies;
   With the angelic host proclaim:
   "Christ is born in Bethlehem!"
      Hark! The herald-angels sing,
      "Glory to the new-born King!"

2. Christ, by highest heaven adored,
   Christ, the everlasting Lord,
   Late in time behold Him come,
   Offspring of a virgin's womb!
   Veiled in flesh the Godhead see!
   Hail, the incarnate Deity!
   Pleased as man with men to dwell,
   Jesus, our Immanuel.
      Hark! The herald-angels sing,
      "Glory to the new-born King!"

3. Hail, the heaven-born Prince of Peace!
   Hail, the Sun of Righteousness!
   Light and life to all He brings,
   Risen with healing in His wings.
   Mild He lays His glory by,
   Born that man no more may die;
   Born to raise the sons of earth,
   Born to give them second birth.
      Hark! The herald-angels sing,
      "Glory to the new-born King!"

70

Ira F Stanphill
© 1968 Singspiration Music/United Nations Music
Publishing/Boosey & Hawkes Ltd

1. **Happiness is to know the Saviour,**
   Living a life within His favour,
   Having a change in my behaviour
   Happiness is the Lord.

2. Happiness is a new creation,
   Jesus and me in close relation,
   Having a part in His salvation,
   Happiness is the Lord

   Real joy is mine,
   No matter if teardrops start;
   I've found the secret,
   It's Jesus in my heart!

3. Happiness is to be forgiven,
   Living a life that's worth the living,
   Taking a trip that leads to heaven,
   Happiness is the Lord,
   Happiness is the Lord,
   Happiness is the Lord!

71

Christian Strover
© M C T Strover / Jubilate Hymns

1. **Have you heard the raindrops drumming**
   on the rooftops?
   Have you heard the raindrops dripping on
      the ground?
   Have you heard the raindrops splashing in
      the streams
   And running to the rivers all around?

   There's water, water of life,
   Jesus gives us the water of life;
   There's water, water of life,
   Jesus gives us the water of life.

2. There's a busy workman digging in the
      desert,
   Digging with a spade that flashes in the
      sun;
   Soon there will be water rising in the
      wellshaft,
   Spilling from the bucket as it comes.
      There's water . . .

3. Nobody can live who hasn't any water,
   When the land is dry then nothing much
      grows;
   Jesus gives us life if we drink the living
      water,
   Sing it so that everybody knows.
      There's water . . .

72

1. **Have you seen the pussy cat, sitting on the**
   wall?
   Have you heard his beautiful purr? *(purr)*
   Have you seen the lion stalking round his
      prey?
   Have you heard his terrible roar? *(roar)*
   One so big, one so small,
   Our heavenly Father cares for them all.
   One so big, one so small,
   Our heavenly Father cares.

2. Have you seen the children coming home
      from school?
   Have you heard them shout hurray?
      (hurray)
   Have you seen the grown-ups coming
      home from work
   Saying 'What a horrible day'? *(what a*
      horrible day)
   Some so big, some so small,
   Our heavenly Father cares for them all.
   Some so big, some so small,
   Our heavenly Father cares.

73

1. **He brought me to His banqueting house,**
   And His banner over me is love.
   (Repeat 3 times)
   His banner over me is love.

   *God loves you and I love you, and that's the
       way it should be.*
   *God loves you and I love you, and that's the
       way it should be.*

2. He feeds me at His banqueting table,
   And His banner over me is love.
   His banner over me is love.
     God loves you . . .

3. He lifts me up to the heavenly places,
   And His banner over me is love.
   His banner over me is love.
     God loves you . . .

4. There's one way to peace through the
       power of the cross,
   And His banner over me is love.
   His banner over me is love.
     God loves you . . .

5. Jesus is the rock of my salvation,
   And His banner over me is love.
   His banner over me is love.
     God loves you . . .

74

1. **He gave me eyes so I could see**
   The wonders of the world.
   Without my eyes I could not see
   The other boys and girls.
   He gave me ears so I could hear
   The wind and rain and sea.
   I've got to tell it to the world,
   He made me.

2. He gave me lips so I could speak
   And say what's in my mind.
   Without my lips I could not speak
   A single word or line.
   He made my mind so I could think,
   And choose what I should be.
   I've got to tell it to the world,
   He made me.

3. He gave me hands so I could touch,
   And hold a thousand things.
   I need my hands to help me write,
   To help me fetch and bring.
   These feet he made so I could run,
   He meant me to be free.
   I've got to tell it to the world,
   He made me.

75

1. **He is Lord,**
   He is Lord,
   He is risen from the dead,
   And He is Lord.
   Ev'ry knee shall bow,
   Ev'ry tongue confess
   That Jesus Christ is Lord.

2. He's my Lord,
   He's my Lord,
   He is risen from the dead,
   And He's my Lord.
   And my knee shall bow,
   And my tongue confess
   That Jesus is my Lord.

76

He made the stars to shine,
He made the rolling sea,
He made the mountains high,
And He made me.
But this is why I love Him,
For me He bled and died,
The Lord of all creation,
Became the crucified.

77

He paid a debt He did not owe,
I owed a debt I could not pay.
I needed someone to wash my sins away,
And now I sing a brand new song,
Amazing grace the whole day long,
For Jesus paid a debt that I could never pay.

78

1. **He's got the whole wide world in His hands,**
   He's got the whole wide world in His hands,
   He's got the whole wide world in His hands,
   He's got the whole world in His hands.

2. He's got ev'rybody here, in His hands,
   He's got ev'rybody here, in His hands,
   He's got ev'rybody here, in His hands,
   He's got the whole world in His hands.

3. He's got the tiny little baby, in His hands,
   He's got the tiny little baby, in His hands,
   He's got the tiny little baby, in His hands,
   He's got the whole world in His hands.

4. He's got you and me brother, in His hands,
   He's got you and me brother, in His hands,
   He's got you and me brother, in His hands,
   He's got the whole world in His hands.

79

1. **He's great! He's God! Jesus Christ is Lord,**
   He's great! He's God! Trust His Word.

2. His Word is truth, for He cannot lie;
   His Word is truth to live by.

3. His love is strong and will never end;
   His love is strong. Praise His Name.

4. He lives evermore as the King of kings;
   He lives evermore. Worship Him.

80

P. Dearmer 1867-1936
after J. Bunyan 1628-1688

1. **He who would valiant be**
   'Gainst all disaster,
   Let him in constancy
   Follow the Master.
   There's no discouragement
   Shall make him once relent,
   His first avowed intent
   To be a pilgrim.

2. Who so beset him round
   With dismal stories,
   Do but themselves confound—
   His strength the more is.
   No foes shall stay his might,
   Though he with giants fight:
   He will make good his right
   To be a pilgrim.

3. Since, Lord, You do defend
   Us with Your Spirit,
   We know we at the end
   Shall life inherit.
   Then fancies flee away!
   I'll fear not what men say,
   I'll labour night and day
   To be a pilgrim.

81

Hévénu shalōm aléchem,
Hévénu shalōm aléchem,
Hévénu shalōm aléchem,
Hévénu shalōm, shalōm,
   shalōm aléchem.

82

How great is our God! How great is his name!
How great is his love, for ever the same!
He rolled back the waters of the mighty Red
   Sea,
And He said, 'I'll never leave you; put your
   trust in me.'

83

How did Moses cross the Red Sea?
How did Moses cross the Red Sea?
How did Moses cross the Red Sea?
How did he get across?
Did he swim? No! No!
Did he row? No! No!
Did he jump? No! No! No! No!
Did he drive? No! No!
Did he fly? No! No!
How did he get across?
God blew with His wind, puff, puff, puff,
   puff.
He blew just enough, 'nough, 'nough,
   'nough, 'nough,
And through the sea He made a path,
That's how he got across.

84

Leonard E. Smith

1. **How lovely on the mountains are the feet of**
   Him
   Who brings good news, good news,
   Proclaiming peace, announcing news of
      happiness,
   Our God reigns, our God reigns, our God
      reigns,
   Our God reigns, our God reigns, our God
      reigns!

2. You watchmen lift your voices joyfully as
      one,
   Shout for your King, your King.
   See eye to eye the Lord restoring Zion:
   Your God reigns, your God reigns, your
      God reigns,
   Your God reigns, your God reigns, your
      God reigns!

3. Waste places of Jerusalem break forth with
      joy,
   We are redeemed, redeemed.
   The Lord has saved and comforted His
      people:
   Your God reigns, your God reigns, your
      God reigns,
   Your God reigns, your God reigns, your
      God reigns!

4. Ends of the earth, see the salvation of your
      God,
   Jesus is Lord, is Lord.
   Before the nations He has bared His holy
      arm:
   Your God reigns, your God reigns, your
      God reigns,
   Your God reigns, your God reigns, your
      God reigns!

85

J.D. Burns 1823-1864
Altered © 1986 Horrobin/Leavers

1. **Hushed was the evening hymn,**
   The temple courts were dark;
   The lamp was burning dim
   Before the sacred ark,
   When suddenly a voice divine
   Rang through the silence of the shrine.

2. The old man, meek and mild,
   The priest of Israel, slept;
   His watch the temple child,
   The little Samuel, kept:
   And what from Eli's sense was sealed
   The Lord to Hannah's son revealed.

3. O give me Samuel's ear,
   The open ear, O Lord,
   Alive and quick to hear
   Each whisper of Your word—
   Like him to answer at Your call,
   And to obey You first of all.

4. O give me Samuel's heart,
   A lowly heart, that waits
   To serve and play the part
   You show us at Your gates
   By day and night, a heart that still
   Moves at the breathing of Your will.

5. O give me Samuel's mind,
   A sweet, unmurmuring faith,
   Obedient and resigned
   To You in life and death,
   That I may read with childlike eyes
   Truths that are hidden from the wise.

86

Frances R. Havergal 1836-1879

1. **I am trusting You, Lord Jesus,**
   You have died for me;
   Trusting You for full salvation
   Great and free.

2. I am trusting You for pardon—
   At Your feet I bow;
   For Your grace and tender mercy,
   Trusting now.

3. I am trusting You for cleansing,
   Jesus, Son of God;
   Trusting You to make me holy
   By Your blood.

4. I am trusting You to guide me—
   You alone shall lead;
   Every day and hour supplying
   All my need.

5. I am trusting You for power—
   Yours can never fail;
   Words which You yourself shall give me
   Must prevail.

6. I am trusting You, Lord Jesus—
   Never let me fall;
   I am trusting You for ever,
   And for all.

87

Graham Kendrick
© 1985 Thankyou Music

**I am a lighthouse, a shining and bright
   house**
Out in the waves of a stormy sea.
The oil of the spirit keeps my lamp burning,
Jesus my Lord is the light in me.
And when people see the good things that I
   do
They'll give praises to God who has sent us
   Jesus.
We'll send out a lifeboat of love and
   forgiveness
And give them a hand to get in.
(Repeat)

While the storm is raging, whoosh, whoosh,
And the wind is blowing, ooo, ooo,
And the waves are crashing, crash! crash!
   crash! crash!

I am a lighthouse, a shining and bright
   house
Out in the waves of a stormy sea.
The oil of the spirit keeps my lamp burning,
Jesus my Lord is the light in me.

88

Philipp Bliss 1838-1876

1. **I am so glad that our Father in heaven**
   Tells of His love in the book He has given:
   Wonderful things in the Bible I see;
   This is the dearest, that Jesus loves me.

   I am so glad that Jesus loves me,
   Jesus loves me, Jesus loves me,
   I am so glad that Jesus loves me,
   Jesus loves even me.

2. Though I forget Him, and wander away,
   He'll always love me wherever I stray;
   Back to His dear loving arms do I flee,
   When I remember that Jesus loves me.
   I am so glad . . .

3. O if there's only one song I can sing,
   When in His beauty I see the great King,
   This shall my song in eternity be,
   O what a wonder that Jesus loves me
   I am so glad . . .

4. If one should ask of me: How can I tell?
   Glory to Jesus, I know very well;
   God's Holy Spirit with mine does agree,
   Constantly witnessing: Jesus loves me.
   I am so glad . . .

89

I am the Way, the Truth and the Life,
That's what Jesus said.
I am the Way, the Truth and the Life,
That's what Jesus said.
Without the Way there is no going,
Without the truth there is no knowing,
Without the Life there is no living,
I am the Way, the Truth and the Life,
That's what Jesus said.

90

I can run through a troop
And leap over a wall,
Hallelujah, (Glory, Glory), Hallelujah,
He's my Prince of Peace,
He gives power to all,
Hallelujah, (Glory, Glory), Hallelujah,
Now there is no condemnation,
Jesus is the rock of my salvation.
I can run through a troop
And leap over a wall,
Hallelujah, (Glory, Glory), Hallelujah.

91

1. **I danced in the morning**
   When the world was begun,
   And I danced in the moon
   And the stars and the sun,
   And I came down from heaven
   And I danced on the earth—
   At Bethlehem I had my birth.

   Dance, then, wherever you may be,
   I am the Lord of the Dance, said he,
   And I'll lead you all, wherever you may be,
   And I'll lead you all in the dance, said He.

2. I danced for the scribe
   And the pharisee,
   But they would not dance
   And they wouldn't follow me.
   I danced for the fishermen,
   For James and John—
   They came with me
   And the dance went on.
   Dance, then, wherever . . .

92

1. **I do not know what lies ahead,**
   The way I cannot see;
   Yet one stands near to be my guide,
   He'll show the way to me:

I know who holds the future,
And He'll guide me with His hand,
With God things don't just happen,
Ev'rything by Him is planned;
So as I face tomorrow
With its problems large and small,
I'll trust the God of miracles,
Give to Him my all.

2. I do not know how many days
   Of life are mine to spend;
   But one who knows and cares for me
   Will keep me to the end:
   I know who holds . . .

3. I do not know the course ahead,
   What joys and griefs are there;
   But one is near who fully knows,
   I'll trust His loving care:
   I know who holds . . .

93

I'll be still and know that You are God;
I'll be still and know You are the Lord;
I'll be still to worship and adore You,
Blessed One, Emmanuel, Jesus.

94

1. **If I were a butterfly,**
   I'd thank You Lord for giving me wings.
   And if I were a robin in a tree,
   I'd thank You Lord that I could sing.
   And if I were a fish in the sea,
   I'd wiggle my tail and I'd giggle with glee,
   But I just thank You Father for making me
   'me'.

   For You gave me a heart
   And You gave me a smile.
   You gave me Jesus and
   You made me Your child.
   And I just thank You Father for making me
   'me'.

2. If I were an elephant,
   I'd thank You Lord by raising my trunk.
   And if I were a kangaroo,
   You know I'd hop right up to You.
   And if I were an octopus,
   I'd thank You Lord for my fine looks,
   But I just thank You Father for making me
   'me'.
   For You gave me . . .

3. If I were a wiggily worm,
   I'd thank You Lord that I could squirm.
   And if I were a billy goat,
   I'd thank You Lord for my strong throat.
   And if I were a fuzzy wuzzy bear,
   I'd thank You Lord for my fuzzy wuzzy hair,
   But I just thank You Father for making me
   'me'.
   For You gave me . . .

95

1. **If you see someone lying in the road,**
   Don't leave him there, give him a hand.
   If you see someone crying in the road
   Don't leave him there, give him a hand.
   Doesn't matter who you are;
   You might be a tramp or a movie-star,
   Just remember whoever you are
   That it's Jesus lying there,
   That it's Jesus crying there.

2. If Jesus sees you lying in the road,
   He won't leave you there, He'll give you a
   hand.
   If Jesus sees you crying in the road,
   He won't leave you there, He'll give you a
   hand.
   Doesn't matter who you are;
   You might be a tramp or a movie-star,
   Just remember whoever you are
   That He sees you lying there,
   And He sees you crying there.

96

If you want joy, real joy, wonderful joy,
Let Jesus come into your heart.
If you want joy, real joy, wonderful joy,
Let Jesus come into your heart.
Your sins He'll take away,
Your night He'll turn to day,
Your heart He'll make over anew,
And then come in to stay.
If you want joy, real joy, wonderful joy,
Let Jesus come into your heart.

97

1. **I gotta home in gloryland that outshines the
   sun,**
   I gotta home in gloryland that outshines the
   sun,
   I gotta home in gloryland that outshines the
   sun,
   Way beyond the blue.

Do Lord, oh do Lord, oh do remember me;
Do Lord, oh do Lord, oh do remember me;
Do Lord, oh do Lord, oh do remember me;
Way beyond the blue.

2. I took Jesus as my saviour, you take Him
   too . . .

3. If you will not bear a cross, you can't wear
   a crown . . .

98

1. **I have decided to follow Jesus,**
   I have decided to follow Jesus,
   I have decided to follow Jesus,
   No turning back, no turning back.

2. The world behind me, the cross before me,
   The world behind me, the cross before me,
   The world behind me, the cross before me,
   No turning back, no turning back.

3. Tho' none go with me, I still will follow,
   Tho' none go with me, I still will follow,
   Tho' none go with me, I still will follow,
   No turning back, no turning back.

4. Will you decide now to follow Jesus?
   Will you decide now to follow Jesus?
   Will you decide now to follow Jesus?
   No turning back, no turning back.

99

1. **I have seen the golden sunshine,**
   I have watched the flowers grow,
   I have listened to the song birds
   And there's one thing now I know,
   They were all put there for us to share
   By someone so divine,
   And if you're a friend of Jesus,
   CLAP CLAP CLAP CLAP
   You're a friend of mine.

   I've seen the light, I've seen the light,
   And that's why my heart sings.
   I've known the joy, I've known the joy
   That loving Jesus brings.

2. I have seen the morning sunshine,
   I have heard the oceans roar,
   I have seen the flowers of springtime,
   And there's one thing I am sure,
   They were all put there for us to share
   By someone so divine,
   And if you're a friend of Jesus,
   CLAP CLAP CLAP CLAP
   You're a friend of mine.
   I've seen the light, . . .

100
Dave Moody
© 1984 C. A. Music/Word Music (UK)

I hear the sound of the army of the Lord,
I hear the sound of the army of the Lord.
It's the sound of praise,
It's the sound of war,
The army of the Lord,
The army of the Lord,
The army of the Lord is marching on.

101
Copyright control

I may never march in the infantry,
Ride with the cavalry, shoot with the
    artillery,
I may never zoom o'er the enemy,
For I'm in the Lord's army.
I'm in the Lord's army (Yes Sir!)
I'm in the Lord's army (Yes Sir!)
I may never march in the infantry,
Ride with the cavalry, shoot with the
    artillery,
I may never zoom o'er the enemy,
For I'm in the Lord's army.

102
Copyright control

I met Jesus at the crossroads,
Where the two ways meet.
Satan too was standing there,
And he said, 'Come this way,
Lots and lots of pleasures
I can give to you today.'
But I said, 'No, there's Jesus here,
Just see what He offers me,
Down here my sins forgiven,
Up there a home in heaven.
Praise God! That's the way for me.'

103
Eric A. Thorn
© Christian Music Ministries

1. **I met You at the cross,**
Jesus my Lord;
I heard You from that cross:
My name You called—
Asked me to follow You all of my days,
Asked me for evermore Your name to
    praise.

2. I saw You on the cross
Dying for me;
I put You on that cross:
But Your one plea—
Would I now follow You all of my days,
And would I evermore Your great name
    praise?

3. Jesus, my Lord and King,
Saviour of all,
Jesus the King of kings,
You heard my call—
That I would follow You all of my days,
And that for evermore Your name I'd praise.

104
© Salvationist Publishing & Supplies

I'm feeding on the living bread,
I'm drinking at the fountain head;
For all who drink, so Jesus said,
Will never, never thirst again.
What, never thirst again?
No! never thirst again.
What, never thirst again!
No! never thirst again.
For all who drink, so Jesus said,
Will never, never thirst again.

105
Oswald J Smith
© 1952, 1980 Zondervan Herman Corp//United
Nations Music Publishing/Boosey & Hawkes Ltd

1. **I'm singing for my Lord ev'rywhere I go,**
Singing of His wondrous love that the world
    may know
How He saved a wretch like me by His
    death on Calvary:
I'm singing for my Lord ev'rywhere I go.

2. I'm singing, but sometimes heavy is the rod,
For this world is not a friend to the grace of
    God;
Yet I sing the whole day long, for He fills
    my heart with song,
I'm singing for my Lord ev'rywhere I go.

3. I'm singing for the lost just because I know
Jesus Christ, whose precious blood washes
    white as snow;
If my songs to Him can bring some lost soul
    I'll gladly sing:
I'm singing for my Lord ev'rywhere I go.

4. I'm singing for the saints as they journey
    home;
Soon they'll reach that happy land where
    they'll never roam,
And with me they'll join and sing praises to
    our Lord and King:
I'm singing for my Lord ev'rywhere I go.

106
Graham Kendrick
© 1985 Thankyou Music

I'm special because God has loved me,
For He gave the best thing that He had to
    save me.
His own Son Jesus, crucified to take the
    blame,
For all the bad things I have done.

Thank you Jesus, thank you Lord,
For loving me so much.
I know I don't deserve anything,
Help me feel your love right now
To know deep in my heart that I'm Your
    special friend.

107

1. **I'm very glad of God:**
   His love takes care of me,
   In every lovely thing I see
   God smiles at me!

2. I'm very glad of God:
   His love takes care of me,
   In every lovely sound I hear
   God speaks to me!

108

1. **In our work and in our play,**
   Jesus, ever with us stay;
   May we serve You all our days,
   True and faithful in our ways.

2. May we in Your strength subdue
   Evil tempers, words untrue,
   Thoughts impure and deeds unkind,
   All things hateful to Your mind.

3. Jesus, from Your throne above,
   Fill anew our hearts with love;
   So that what we say and do
   Shows that we belong to You.

4. Children of the King are we,
   May we loyal to Him be:
   Try to please Him every day,
   In our work and in our play.

109

In my need Jesus found me,
Put His strong arm around me,
Brought me safe home,
Into the shelter of the fold.
Gracious Shepherd that sought me,
Precious life-blood that bought me;
Out of the night,
Into the light and near to God.

110

1. **Infant holy,**
   Infant lowly.
   For his bed a cattle stall;
   Oxen lowing,
   Little knowing
   Christ the Babe is Lord of all.

Swift are winging
Angels singing,
Nowells ringing,
Tidings bringing,
Christ the Babe is Lord of all.
Christ the Babe is Lord of all.

2. Flocks were sleeping,
   Shepherds keeping
   Vigil till the morning new.
   Saw the glory,
   Heard the story,
   Tidings of a gospel true.
   Thus rejoicing,
   Free from sorrow,
   Praises voicing,
   Greet the morrow,
   Christ the Babe was born for you!
   Christ the Babe was born for you!

111

In the name of Jesus,
In the name of Jesus,
We have the victory.
In the name of Jesus,
In the name of Jesus,
Demons will have to flee.
Who can tell what God can do?
Who can tell of His love for you?
In the name of Jesus, Jesus,
We have the victory.

112

In the stars His handiwork I see,
On the wind He speaks with majesty;
Though He's ruling over land and sea,
What is that to me?
I will celebrate nativity,
For it has a place in history,
Sure, Christ came to set His people free.
What is that to me?
Then by faith I met Him face to face,
And I felt the wonder of His grace,
Then I knew that He was more than just a
    God
Who didn't care, who lived away up there.
And now He lives within me day by day,
Ever watching o'er me lest I stray,
Helping me to find the narrow way,
He's ev'rything to me.

113

1. **I serve a risen Saviour,**
   He's in the world today;
   I know that He is living,
   Whatever men may say;

I see His hand of mercy,
I hear His voice of cheer.
And just the time I need Him
He's always near.

He lives, He lives,
Christ Jesus lives today!
He walks with me and talks with me
Along life's narrow way.
He lives, He lives,
Salvation to impart!
You ask me how I know He lives,
He lives within my heart.

2. In all the world around me
I see His loving care,
And tho' my heart grows weary
I never will despair;
I know that He is leading,
Thro' all the stormy blast,
The day of His appearing
Will come at last.
    He lives, . . .

3. Rejoice, rejoice, O Christian,
Lift up your voice and sing
Eternal hallelujahs
To Jesus Christ the King!
The Hope of all who seek Him,
The Help of all who find,
None other is so loving,
So good and kind.
    He lives, . . .

114   Copyright control

Isaiah heard the voice of the Lord
And he said, 'Here am I send me.'
He loved to do the will of the Lord, so he
    said,
'Here am I send me; here am I send me;
Anywhere for Thee.'
So when I hear the voice of the Lord,
I will say, here am I, send me.

115   © L. Scott b. 1898

1. **I sing a song of the saints of God,**
Patient and brave and true,
Who toiled and fought and lived and died
For the Lord they loved and knew.
And one was a doctor, and one was a
    queen,
And one was a shepherdess on the green:
They were all of them saints of God; and I
    mean,
God helping, to be one too.

2. They loved their God so good and dear,
And His love made them strong;
And they followed the right, for Jesus' sake,
The whole of their good lives long.
And one was a soldier, and one was a
    priest,
And one was slain by a fierce wild beast:
And there's not any reason, no, not in the
    least,
Why I shouldn't be one too.

3. They lived not only in ages past,
There are hundreds of thousands still;
The world is bright with the joyous saints
Who love to do Jesus' will.
You can meet them in school, or in lanes,
    or at sea,
In church, or in trains, or in shops, or at
    tea,
For the saints of God began just like me,
And I mean to be one too.

116   E.H. Sears 1810-1876
© in this version Jubilate Hymns

1. **It came upon the midnight clear,**
That glorious song of old,
From angels bending near the earth
To touch their harps of gold:
'Peace on the earth, goodwill to men
From heaven's all-gracious king!'
The world in solemn stillness lay
To hear the angels sing.

2. With sorrow brought by sin and strife
The world has suffered long
And, since the angels sang, have passed
Two thousand years of wrong:
For man at war with man hears not
The love-song which they bring:
O hush the noise, you men of strife,
And hear the angels sing!

3. And those whose journey now is hard,
Whose hope is burning low,
Who tread the rocky path of life
With painful steps and slow:
O listen to the news of love
Which makes the heavens ring!
O rest beside the weary road
And hear the angels sing!

4. And still the days are hastening on—
By prophets seen of old—
Towards the fulness of the time
When comes the age foretold:
Then earth and heaven renewed shall see
The Prince of Peace, their king;
And all the world repeat the song
Which now the angels sing.

117

W.W. How 1823-1897
© in this version Jubilate Hymns

1. **It is a thing most wonderful**
   Almost too wonderful to be
   That God's own Son should come from
      heaven
   And die to save a child like me.

2. And yet I know that it is true
   He came to this poor world below
   And wept and toiled, and mourned and died
   Only because He loved us so.

3. I cannot tell how He could love
   A child so weak and full of sin;
   His love must be so wonderful
   If He could die my love to win.

4. I sometimes think about the cross,
   And shut my eyes, and try to see
   The cruel nails, and crown of thorns,
   And Jesus crucified for me.

5. But, even could I see Him die
   I could but see a little part
   Of that great love which, like a fire,
   Is always burning in His heart.

6. How wonderful it is to know
   His love for me so free and sure;
   But yet more wonderful to see
   My love for Him so faint and poor.

7. And yet I want to love you, Lord:
   O teach me how to grow in grace,
   That I may love you more and more
   Until I see you face to face.

118

Gary Pfeiffer
© 1973 Fred Bock Music Co / Thankyou Music

1. **It's a happy day and I praise God for the**
   weather.
   It's a happy day living it for my Lord.
   It's a happy day things are gonna get better
   Living each day by the promises in God's
   Word.

2. It's a grumpy day and I can't stand the
      weather
   It's a grumpy day living it for myself
   It's a grumpy day and things aren't going to
      get better
   Living each day with my Bible up on my
      shelf.

3. It's a happy day and I praise God for the
      weather.
   It's a happy day living it for my Lord.
   It's a happy day things are gonna get better
   Living each day by the promises in God's
   Word.

119

It's me, it's me, it's me, O Lord,
Standin' in the need of prayer.
It's me, it's me, it's me, O Lord,
Standin' in the need of prayer.

1. Not my brother or my sister, but it's me, O
      Lord,
   Standin' in the need of prayer.
   Not my brother or my sister, but it's me, O
      Lord,
   Standin' in the need of prayer.
    It's me, it's me, . . .

2. Not my mother or my father, but it's me, O
      Lord,
   Standin' in the need of prayer.
   Not my mother or my father, but it's me, O
      Lord,
   Standin' in the need of prayer.
    It's me, it's me, . . .

3. Not my stranger or my neighbour, but it's
      me, O Lord,
   Standin' in the need of prayer.
   Not my stranger or my neighbour, but it's
      me, O Lord,
   Standin' in the need of prayer.
    It's me, it's me, . . .

120

I've got peace like a river,
Peace like a river,
I've got peace like a river
In my soul.
I've got peace like a river,
Peace like a river,
I've got peace like a river,
In my soul.

121

Copyright control

1. **I've got that joy, joy, joy, joy,**
   Down in my heart, (Where?)
   Down in my heart, (Where?)
   Down in my heart,
   I've got that joy, joy, joy, joy,
   Down in my heart, (Where?)
   Down in my heart to stay.

   And I'm so happy,
   So very happy,
   I've got the love of Jesus in my heart
   And I'm so happy, so very happy,
   I've got the love of Jesus in my heart

2. I've got the peace that passes
     understanding
   Down in my heart, (Where?)
   Down in my heart, (Where?)
   Down in my heart,
   I've got the peace that passes
     understanding
   Down in my heart, (Where?)
   Down in my heart to stay.
     And I'm so happy . . .

122

1. **I want to live for Jesus ev'ry day. (ev'ry**
   day)
   I want to live for Jesus, come what may.
     (come what may)
   Take the world and all its pleasure, I've got
     a more enduring treasure.
   I want to live for Jesus ev'ry day.

2. I'm gonna live for Jesus ev'ry day. (ev'ry
     day)
   I'm gonna live for Jesus come what may.
     (come what may)
   Take the world and all its pleasure, I've got
     a more enduring treasure.
   I'm gonna live for Jesus ev'ry day.

123

I will make you fishers of men,
Fishers of men, fishers of men;
I will make you fishers of men,
If you follow Me,
If you follow Me, If you follow Me;
I will make you fishers of men,
If you follow Me.

124

1. **I want to walk with Jesus Christ,**
   All the days I live of this life on earth,
   To give to Him complete control
   Of body and of soul:

   Follow Him, follow Him, yield your life to
     Him,
   He has conquered death, He is King of
     Kings,
   Accept the joy which He gives to those
   Who yield their lives to Him.

2. I want to learn to speak to Him
   To pray to Him, confess my sin,
   To open my life and let Him in,
   For joy will then be mine:
     Follow Him, follow Him, . . .

3. I want to learn to speak of Him,
   My life must show that He lives in me,
   My deeds, my thoughts, my words must speak
   All of His love for me:
     Follow Him, follow Him, . . .

4. I want to learn to read His Word,
   For this is how I know the way
   To live my life as pleases Him,
   In holiness and joy:
     Follow Him, follow Him, . . .

5. O Holy Spirit of the Lord,
   Enter now into this heart of mine,
   Take full control of my selfish will
   And make me wholly Thine:
     Follow Him, follow Him, . . .

125

1. **I was lost but Jesus found me,**
   Found the sheep that went astray.
   Threw His loving arms around me,
   Drew me back into His way

   Alleluia, Alleluia,
   Alleluia, Alleluia,
   Alleluia.

2. Glory, glory, alleluia,
   Come and bless the Lord our King,
   Glory, glory, alleluia,
   With His praise all heaven rings.
     Alleluia, Alleluia, . . .

126

1. **I will sing, I will sing a song unto the Lord.**
   I will sing, I will sing a song unto the Lord.
   I will sing, I will sing a song unto the Lord.
   Alleluia, glory to the Lord.

   Allelu, alleluia, glory to the Lord.
   Allelu, alleluia, glory to the Lord.
   Allelu, alleluia, glory to the Lord.
   Alleluia, glory to the Lord.

2. We will come, we will come as one before
     the Lord.
   We will come, we will come as one before
     the Lord.
   We will come, we will come as one before
     the Lord.
   Alleluia, glory to the Lord.
     Allelu, alleluia . . .

3. If the Son, if the Son shall make you free,
   If the Son, if the Son shall make you free,
   If the Son, if the Son shall make you free,
   You shall be free indeed.
     Allelu, alleluia . . .

4. They that sow in tears shall reap in joy,
   They that sow in tears shall reap in joy,
   They that sow in tears shall reap in joy,
   Alleluia, glory to the Lord.
   Allelu, alleluia . . .

5. Ev'ry knee shall bow and ev'ry tongue
      confess,
   Ev'ry knee shall bow and ev'ry tongue
      confess,
   Ev'ry knee shall bow and ev'ry tongue
      confess
   That Jesus Christ is Lord.
   Allelu, alleluia . . .

6. In His name, in His name we have the
      victory.
   In His name, in His name we have the
      victory.
   In His name, in His name we have the
      victory.
   Alleluia, glory to the Lord.
   Allelu, alleluia . . .

127
F H Rawley 1854-1952
© Marshall Morgan & Scott / HarperCollins*Religious*

1. **I will sing the wondrous story**
   Of the Christ who died for me,—
   How He left the realms of glory
   For the cross on Calvary.
   Yes, I'll sing the wondrous story
   Of the Christ who died for me,—
   Sing it with His saints in glory,
   Gathered by the crystal sea.

2. I was lost: but Jesus found me,
   Found the sheep that went astray,
   Raised me up and gently led me
   Back into the narrow way.
   Days of darkness still may tread;
   Sorrow's paths I oft may tread;
   But His presence still is with me,
   By His guiding hand I'm led.

3. He will keep me till the river
   Rolls its waters at my feet:
   Then He'll bear me safely over,
   Made by grace for glory meet.
   Yes, I'll sing the wondrous story
   Of the Christ who died for me,—
   Sing it with His saints in glory,
   Gathered by the crystal sea.

128
Susan Warner 1819-1885

1. **Jesus bids us shine**
   With a pure, clear light,
   Like a little candle
   Burning in the night.
   In this world is darkness;
   So let us shine,
   You in your small corner,
   And I in mine.

2. Jesus bids us shine,
   First of all for Him;
   Well He sees and knows it,
   If our light grows dim.
   He looks down from heaven
   To see us shine,
   You in your small corner,
   And I in mine

3. Jesus bids us shine,
   Then, for all around;
   Many kinds of darkness
   In the world are found—
   Sin, and want and sorrow;
   So we must shine,
   You in your small corner,
   And I in mine.

129
Copyright control

Jesus Christ is alive today,
I know, I know it's true.
Sov reign of the Universe,
I give Him homage due.
Seated there at God's right hand,
I am with Him in the promised land.
Jesus lives and reigns in me,
That's how I know it's true.

130
Lyra Davidica 1708

1. **Jesus Christ is risen today, Hallelujah!**
   Our triumphant holy day, Hallelujah!
   Who did once, upon the cross, Hallelujah!
   Suffer to redeem our loss. Hallelujah!

2. Hymns of praise then let us sing,
      Hallelujah!
   Unto Christ, our heavenly King, Hallelujah!
   Who endured the cross and grave,
      Hallelujah!
   Sinners to redeem and save. Hallelujah!

3. But the pains which He endured,
      Hallelujah!
   Our salvation have procured, Hallelujah!
   Now in heaven above He's King,
      Hallelujah!
   Where the angels ever sing Hallelujah!

131

After German authors
(from the fifteenth century)
© Michael Perry / Jubilate Hymns

1. **Jesus Christ the Lord is born,**
   All the bells are ringing!
   Angels greet the holy One
   And shepherds hear them singing,
   And shepherds hear them singing:

2. 'Go to Bethlehem today,
   Find your King and Saviour:
   Glory be to God on high,
   To earth his peace and favour,
   To earth his peace and favour!'

3. Held within a cattle stall,
   Loved by love maternal,
   See the master of us all,
   Our Lord of lords eternal,
   Our Lord of lords eternal!

4. Soon shall come the wise men three,
   Rousing Herod's anger;
   Mother's hearts shall broken be
   And Mary's son in danger,
   And Mary's son in danger.

5. Death from life and life from death,
   Our salvation's story:
   Let all living things give breath
   To Christmas songs of glory,
   To Christmas songs of glory!

132

Jesus died for all the children,
All the children of the world;
Red and yellow, black and white,
All are precious in His sight:
Jesus died for all the children of the world.

133

Dave Bolton
© 1975 Thankyou Music

Jesus, how lovely You are!
You are so gentle so pure and kind,
You shine like the morning star:
Jesus how lovely You are.

1. Alleluia, Jesus is my Lord and King.
   Alleluia, Jesus is my everything.
   Jesus, how lovely . . .

2. Alleluia, Jesus died and rose again;
   Alleluia, Jesus forgave all my sin.
   Jesus, how lovely . . .

3. Alleluia, Jesus is meek and lowly;
   Alleluia, Jesus is pure and holy.
   Jesus, how lovely . . .

4. Alleluia, Jesus is the bridegroom;
   Alleluia, Jesus will take His bride soon.
   Jesus, how lovely . . .

134

Margaret Cropper
© Stainer & Bell Ltd.

1. **Jesus' hands were kind hands, doing good to all,**
   healing pain and sickness, blessing children small,
   washing tired feet and saving those who fall;
   Jesus' hands were kind hands, doing good to all.

2. Take my hands Lord Jesus, let them work for You;
   make them strong and gentle, kind in all I do;
   let me watch You, Jesus, till I'm gentle too,
   till my hands are kind hands, quick to work for You.

135

© Gordon Brattle

Jesus is knocking, patiently waiting,
Outside your heart's closed door.
Do not reject Him, simply accept Him,
Now and forever more.

136

Paul Mazak
© 1974, 1975 Celebration/Thankyou Music

1. **Jesus is a friend of mine**
   Praise Him!
   Jesus is a friend of mine
   Praise Him!
   Praise Him! Praise Him!
   Jesus is a friend of mine
   Praise Him!

2. Jesus died to set us free
   Praise Him!
   Jesus died to set us free
   Praise Him!
   Praise Him! Praise Him!
   Jesus died to set us free
   Praise Him!

3. Jesus is the King of Kings
   Praise Him!
   Jesus is the King of Kings
   Praise Him!
   Praise Him! Praise Him!
   Jesus is the King of Kings
   Praise Him!

137

David J. Mansell
© 1980 Springtide/Word Music (UK)

1. **Jesus is Lord! Creation's voice proclaims it,**
   For by his power each tree and flower was planned and made
   Jesus is Lord! The universe declares it.
   Sun, moon and stars in heaven cry Jesus is Lord!

Jesus is Lord! Jesus is Lord!
Praise Him with 'Hallelujahs' for Jesus is
* Lord!*

2. Jesus is Lord! Yet from his throne eternal
   In flesh He came to die in pain on Calv'ry's
       tree.
   Jesus is Lord! From Him all life
       proceeding,
   Yet gave his life a ransom thus setting us
       free.
   Jesus is Lord! . . .

3. Jesus is Lord! O'er sin the mighty
       conqueror,
   From death He rose and all his foes shall
       own his name.
   Jesus is Lord! God sends his Holy Spirit
   To show by works of power that Jesus is
       Lord.
   Jesus is Lord! . . .

138

Jesus I will come with You,
I will follow in Your way.
I will trust You,
I will bring You all I have today.
Jesus, You're the Way,
Jesus, You're the Truth,
Jesus, You're the Life.
Praise Your name.

139

Jesus' love is very wonderful,
Jesus' love is very wonderful,
Jesus' love is very wonderful,
O wonderful love!
So high, you can't get over it,
So low, you can't get under it,
So wide, you can't get round it,
O wonderful love!

140

Anna Warner 1827-1915

1. **Jesus loves me! this I know,**
   For the Bible tells me so;
   Little ones to Him belong;
   They are weak, but He is strong.

   Yes! Jesus loves me!
   Yes! Jesus loves me!
   Yes! Jesus loves me!
   The Bible tells me so.

2. Jesus loves me! He who died
   Heaven's gate to open wide;
   He will wash away my sin,
   Let His little child come in.
       Yes! Jesus loves me! . . .

3. Jesus loves me! He will stay
   Close beside me all the way;
   Then His little child will take
   Up to heaven, for His dear sake.
       Yes! Jesus loves me! . . .

141

Jesus, Name above all names.
Beautiful Saviour,
Glorious Lord, Emmanuel,
God is with us,
Blessed Redeemer,
Living Word.

142

1. **Jesus said that whosoever will,**
   Whosoever will, whosoever will.
   Jesus said that whosoever will,
   Whosoever will may come.

2. I'm so glad that He included me,
   He included me, He included me.
   I'm so glad that He included me,
   When Jesus said that whosoever will may
       come.

143

Joshua fit the battle of Jericho,
Jericho, Jericho,
Joshua fit the battle of Jericho,
And the walls came tumbling down.

1. You may talk about your king of Gideon,
   You may talk about your man of Saul,
   But there's none like good old Joshua   ,
   At the battle of Jericho.

2. Up to the walls of Jericho
   He marched with spear in hand.
   'Go blow them ram-horns,' Joshua cried,
   'Cause the battle am in my hand.'

3. Then the ram-sheeps' horns began to blow,
   Trumpets began to sound.
   Joshua commanded the children to shout,
   And the walls came tumbling down, that
       morning.

   Joshua fit the battle of Jericho,
   Jericho, Jericho,
   Joshua fit the battle of Jericho,
   And the walls came tumbling down.

144

**Joy is the flag flown high from the castle of
my heart,**
From the castle of my heart, from the castle
of my heart.
Joy is the flag flown high from the castle of
my heart,
When the King is in residence there.
So let it fly in the sky, let the whole world
know,
Let the whole world know, let the whole
world know.
So let it fly in the sky, let the whole world
know,
That the King is in residence there.

145

Jubilate, ev'rybody,
Serve the Lord in all your ways,
And come before His presence singing;
Enter now His courts with praise.
For the Lord our God is gracious,
And His mercy everlasting.
Jubilate, jubilate,
Jubilate Deo!

146

1. **Just as I am, Your child to be,**
   Friend of the young, who died for me;
   To give my life wholeheartedly,
   O Jesus Christ I come.

2. While I am still a child today,
   I give my life, my work and play
   To Him alone, without delay,
   With all my heart I come.

3. I see in Jesus Christ the light,
   With Him as Lord, and in His might
   I turn from sin to what is right,
   My Lord to You I come.

4. Lord, take my dreams of fame and gold,
   I accept now a life controlled
   By faith in You as days unfold,
   With my whole life I come.

5. Just as I am, young, strong and free,
   To be the best that I can be,
   That others may see You in me,
   Lord of my life I come.

147

Keep me shining, Lord,
Keep me shining, Lord,
In all I say and do;
That the world may see
Christ lives in me,
And learn to love Him too.

148

King of Kings and Lord of Lords,
Glory, hallelujah!
King of Kings and Lord of Lords,
Glory, hallelujah!
Jesus, Prince of Peace,
Glory, hallelujah!
Jesus, Prince of Peace,
Glory, hallelujah!

149

1. **Kum ba yah, my Lord, Kum ba yah.**
   Kum ba yah, my Lord, Kum ba yah.
   Kum ba yah, my Lord, Kum ba yah.
   O Lord, Kum ba yah.

2. Someone's crying Lord, Kum ba yah.
   Someone's crying Lord, Kum ba yah.
   Someone's crying Lord, Kum ba yah.
   O Lord, Kum ba yah.

3. Someone's singing Lord, Kum ba yah.
   Someone's singing Lord, Kum ba yah.
   Someone's singing Lord, Kum ba yah.
   O Lord, Kum ba yah.

4. Someone's praying Lord, Kum ba yah.
   Someone's praying Lord, Kum ba yah.
   Someone's praying Lord, Kum ba yah.
   O Lord, Kum ba yah.

5. Hear our prayer, O Lord, hear our prayer,
   Keep our friends, O Lord, in Your care;
   Keep our friends, O Lord, in Your care.
   O Lord, Kum ba yah.

150

Let's talk about Jesus,
The King of kings is He,
The Lord of lords supreme,
Thro' all eternity.
The Great I AM, the Way,
The Truth, the Life, the Door.
Let's talk about Jesus more and more.

151 Graham Kendrick
© 1985 Thankyou Music

1. **Led like a lamb**
To the slaughter
In silence and shame
There on Your back
You carried a world
Of violence and pain
Bleeding, dying,
Bleeding, dying.

You're alive
You're alive
You have risen!
Alleluia
And the power
And the glory
Is given
Alleluia
Jesus to You.

2. At break of dawn
Poor Mary
Still weeping she came
When through her grief
She heard Your voice
Now speaking her name
Mary, Master,
Mary, Master.
    You're alive . . .

3. At the right hand
Of the Father
Now seated on high
You have begun
Your eternal reign
Of justice and joy
Glory, glory,
Glory, glory.
    You're alive . . .

152 J E Seddon
© 1969 Mrs Mavis Seddon / Jubilate Hymns

1. **Let us praise God together,**
Let us praise,
Let us praise God together,
Him proclaim.
He is faithful in all His ways,
He is worthy of all our praise,
His Name be exalted on high.

2. Let us seek God together,
Let us pray,
Let us seek His forgiveness
As we pray.
He will cleanse us from all sin,
He will help us the fight to win,
His Name be exalted on high.

3. Let us serve God together,
Let us serve;
Let our lives show His goodness
As we work.
Christ the Lord is the world's true light,
Let us serve Him with all our might;
His Name be exalted on high.

153 Marcus Uzilevsky
© Oaksprings Impressions

Live, live, live,
Live, live, live,
Jesus is living in my soul.
Live, live, live,
Live, live, live,
Jesus is living in my soul.

1. Hanging on the tree,
He prayed for you and me.
Jesus is living in my soul.
To His spirit yield,
By His stripes we're healed.
Jesus is living in my soul.
    Live, live, live . . .

2. He took me out of darkness,
And He set me free.
Jesus is living in my soul.
Once I was blind,
Now I can see.
Jesus is living in my soul.
    Live, live, live . . .

3. Gonna shout and sing,
Let the hallelujah ring.
Jesus is living in my soul.
I'm gonna shout and sing,
There's healing in His wing.
Jesus is living in my soul.
    Live, live, live . . .

154 John Milton

1. **Let us with a gladsome mind**
Praise the Lord, for He is kind:

For His mercies still endure,
Ever faithful, ever sure.

2. He, with all-commanding might,
Filled the new-made world with light:
    For His mercies . . .

3. All things living He does feed,
His full hand supplies their need:
    For His mercies . . .

4. Let us then, with gladsome mind
Praise the Lord, for He is kind:
    For His mercies . . .

155

John Fawcett 1740-1817
Altered © 1986 Horrobin/Leavers

1. **Lord dismiss us with Your blessing,**
   Fill our hearts with joy and peace.
   Let us each, Your love possessing,
   Triumph in redeeming grace;
   O refresh us, O refresh us
   As to serve we leave this place.

2. Thanks we give and adoration,
   For Your gospel's joyful sound;
   May the fruits of Your salvation
   In our hearts and lives abound;
   So Your presence, so Your presence
   Will with us always be found.

156

Patrick Appleford b. 1925
© 1960 Josef Weinberger Ltd

1. **Lord Jesus Christ,**
   You have come to us,
   You are one with us,
   Mary's Son.
   Cleansing our souls from all their sin,
   Pouring Your love and goodness in,
   Jesus, our love for You we sing,
   Living Lord.

2. Lord Jesus Christ,
   Now and every day
   Teach us how to pray,
   Son of God.
   You have commanded us to do
   This, in remembrance, Lord, of You:
   Into our lives Your power breaks through,
   Living Lord.

3. Lord Jesus Christ,
   You have come to us,
   Born as one of us,
   Mary's Son.
   Led out to die on Calvary,
   Risen from death to set us free,
   Living Lord Jesus, help us see
   You are Lord.

4. Lord Jesus Christ,
   I would come to You.
   Live my life for You,
   Son of God.
   All Your commands I know are true,
   Your many gifts will make me new,
   Into my life Your power breaks through,
   Living Lord.

157

Jan Struther d. 1953
© from Enlarged Songs of Praise
By permission Oxford University Press

1. **Lord of all hopefulness, Lord of all joy,**
   Whose trust, ever child-like, no cares could
      destroy,
   Be there at our waking, and give us, we
      pray,
   Your peace in our hearts, Lord, at the break
      of the day.

2. Lord of all eagerness, Lord of all faith,
   Whose strong hands were skilled at the
      plane and the lathe,
   Be there at our labours, and give us, we
      pray,
   Your strength in our hearts, Lord, at the
      noon of the day.

3. Lord of all kindliness, Lord of all grace,
   Your hands swift to welcome, Your arms to
      embrace,
   Be there at our homing, and give us, we
      pray,
   Your love in our hearts, Lord, at the eve of
      the day.

4. Lord of all gentleness, Lord of all calm,
   Whose voice is contentment, whose
      presence is balm,
   Be there at our sleeping, and give us, we
      pray,
   Your peace in our hearts, Lord, at the end
      of the day.

158

© 1985 Andy Silver

Love, joy, peace and patience, kindness,
Goodness, meekness, faith, self-control.
These are the fruit of God's Holy Spirit
And against such there is no Law.
Those who belong to Christ should now live
   this way,
Walking in the Spirit each day.
So praise Him, praise Him, give Him all the
   glory,
Walking in the Spirit each day.

159

Robert Lowry 1826-1899

1. **Low in the grave He lay,**
   Jesus, my Saviour;
   Waiting the coming day,
   Jesus, my Lord.

Up from the grave He arose,
With a mighty triumph o'er His foes;
He arose a Victor from the dark domain,
And He lives for ever with His saints to
    reign:
He arose! He arose! Hallelujah! Christ
    arose!

2. Vainly they watch His bed,
   Jesus, my Saviour;
   Vainly they seal the dead,
   Jesus, my Lord.
     Up from the grave . . .

3. Death cannot keep his prey,
   Jesus my Saviour;
   He tore the bars away,
   Jesus, my Lord.
     Up from the grave . . .

160

Majesty, worship His Majesty;
Unto Jesus be glory, honour and praise.
Majesty, kingdom authority, flows from His
    throne
Unto His own, His anthem raise.
So exalt, lift up on high, the name of Jesus
Magnify, come glorify, Christ Jesus the
    King.
Majesty, worship His Majesty
Jesus who died, now glorified, King of all
    kings.

161

1. **Make me a channel of Your peace.**
   Where there is hatred let me bring Your
       love;
   Where there is injury, Your pardon, Lord;
   And where there's doubt, true faith in You.

   Oh, Master, grant that I may never seek
   So much to be consoled as to console;
   To be understood as to understand;
   To be loved, as to love with all my soul.

2. Make me a channel of Your peace.
   Where there's despair in life let me bring
       hope;
   Where there is darkness, only light;
   And where there's sadness, ever joy.
     Oh, Master, grant...

3. Make me a channel of Your peace.
   It is in pardoning that we are pardoned,
   In giving to all men that we receive;
   And in dying that we're born to eternal life.

162

Make me a servant, humble and meek,
Lord, let me lift up those who are weak.
And may the prayer of my heart always be:
Make me a servant, make me a servant,
Make me a servant today.

163

Make the Book live to me, O Lord,
Show me Yourself within Your Word,
Show me myself and show me my Saviour,
And make the Book live to me.

164

Mary had a little baby, Mary had a little
    baby;
Here and there and everywhere the angels
    sang
Praise the Lord.
Mary had a little baby, Mary had a little
    baby;
Here and there and everywhere the angels
    sang
Praise the Lord.
Glory, glory, glory, glory,
Everybody sing the song.
Glory, glory, glory, glory,
God's Son has come to earth.
Mary had a little baby, Mary had a little
    baby;
Here and there and everywhere the angels
    sang
Praise the Lord.

165

1. **May the mind of Christ my Saviour**
   Live in me from day to day,
   By His love and power controlling
   All I do or say.

2. May the word of God dwell richly
   In my heart from hour to hour,
   So that all may see I triumph
   Only through His power.

3. May the peace of God my Father
   Rule my life in everything,
   That I may be calm to comfort
   Sick and sorrowing.

4. May the love of Jesus fill me,
   As the waters fill the sea;
   Him uplifting, self-denying,
   This is victory.

5. May I run the race before me,
   Strong and brave onward I go,
   Looking only unto Jesus
   As in Him I grow.

166

1. **Morning has broken**
   Like the first morning,
   Blackbird has spoken
   Like the first bird.
   Praise for the singing!
   Praise for the morning!
   Praise for them, springing
   Fresh from the Lord!

2. Mine is the sunlight!
   Mine is the morning
   Here in the bright light
   Of this fair day!
   Praise with elation,
   Praise every morning
   God's re-creation
   Of the new day!

167
Copyright control

1. **Mister Noah built an ark,**
   The people thought it such a lark,
   Mister Noah pleaded so
   But into the ark they would not go.

   Down came the rain in torrents,
   (splish, splash)
   Down came the rain in torrents,
   (splish, splash)
   Down came the rain in torrents,
   And only eight were saved.

2. The animals went in two by two,
   Elephant, giraffe and kangaroo.
   All were safely stowed away
   On that great and aweful day.

   Down came the rain in torrents,
   (splish, splash)
   Down came the rain in torrents,
   (splish, splash)
   Down came the rain in torrents,
   And only eight were saved.

   Whenever you see a rainbow,
   Whenever you see a rainbow,
   Whenever you see a rainbow,
   Remember God is love.

168
Thomas Toke Lynch 1818-1871
Altered © 1986 Horrobin/Leavers

1. **My faith is like a staff of oak,**
   The traveller's well-loved aid;
   My faith, it is a weapon strong,
   The soldier's trusty blade.
   I'll travel on, and still be stirred
   To action at my Master's word;
   By all life's perils undeterred,
   A soldier unafraid.

2. My faith is like a staff of oak,
   O let me on it lean!
   My faith, it is a sharpened sword,
   May falsehood find it keen.
   Now fill me with Your Spirit Lord,
   Teach and change me through Your word,
   And by Your love may I be stirred,
   As all true saints have been.

169
Copyright control

1. **My God is so big, so strong and so mighty,**
   There's nothing that He cannot do.
   (repeat)
   The rivers are His, the mountains are His,
   The stars are His handiwork too.
   My God is so big, so strong and so mighty,
   There's nothing that He cannot do.

2. My God is so big, so strong and so mighty,
   There's nothing that He cannot do.
   (repeat)
   He's called you to live, for Him ev'ry day,
   In all that you say and you do.
   My God is so big, so strong and so mighty,
   He can do all things through you.

170

My Lord is higher than a mountain,
He is stronger than an army,
He is wiser than any man can tell.
My Lord is faster than a rocket,
Can see more than a telescope,
Is bigger than the universe as well.
His love is warmer than the burning sun,
Closer than the nearest friend,
More real than any truth can be.
My Lord, He knows about the past,
And He knows about the future,
And He also knows all about me.

171

J. Keble 1792-1866

1. **New every morning is the love**
   Our waking and uprising prove:
   Through sleep and darkness safely
      brought,
   Restored to life and power and thought.

2. New mercies, each returning day,
   Surround your people as they pray:
   New dangers past, new sins forgiven,
   New thoughts of God, new hopes of
      heaven.

3. If in our daily life our mind
   Be set to honour all we find,
   New treasures still, of countless price,
   God will provide for sacrifice.

4. The trivial round, the common task,
   Will give us all we ought to ask:
   Room to deny ourselves, a road
   To bring us daily nearer God.

5. Prepare us, Lord, in Your dear love
   For perfect rest with You above,
   And help us, this and every day,
   To grow more like You as we pray.

172

© J.H. Cansdale
Altered © 1985 Horrobin/Leavers

Now be strong and very courageous,
For I have commanded you.
Be not afraid
Be not dismayed;
You will have victory.
I will be with you until the end,
Captain and Leader,
Guide and Friend.

173

S. Baring-Gould
Altered © 1986 Horrobin/Leavers

1. **Now the day is over,**
   Night will soon be here,
   Help me to remember
   You are always near.

2. As the darkness gathers,
   Stars shine overhead,
   Creatures, birds and flowers
   Rest their weary heads.

3. Father, give all people
   Calm and peaceful rest,
   Through Your gracious presence
   May our sleep be blessed.

4. Comfort every sufferer
   Watching late in pain;
   Those who plan some evil
   From their sin restrain.

5. When the morning wakes me,
   Ready for the day,
   Help me, Lord, to serve you,
   Walking in your way.

6. Glory to the Father,
   Glory to the Son;
   And to the Holy Spirit
   Blessing everyone.

174

J.M.C. Crum 1872-1958
From the Oxford Book of Carols
Oxford University Press

1. **Now the green blade riseth from the buried
   grain,**
   Wheat that in the dark earth many days has
      lain.
   Love lives again, that with the dead has
      been;
   Love is come again, like wheat that
      springeth green.

2. In the grave they laid him, Love whom men
      had slain,
   Thinking that never He would wake again;
   Laid in the earth like grain that sleeps
      unseen,
   Love is come again, like wheat that
      springeth green.

3. Forth he came at Easter, like the risen
      grain,
   He that for three days in the grave had lain.
   Quick from the dead my risen Lord is seen;
   Love is come again, like wheat that
      springeth green.

4. When our hearts are wintry, grieving, or in
      pain,
   Your touch can call us back to life again.
   Fields of our hearts that dead and bare
      have been;
   Love is come again, like wheat that
      springeth green.

175

Martin Rinkart 1586-1649
tr. by Katherine Winkworth 1829-1878
Altered © 1986 Horrobin/Leavers.

1. **Now thank we all our God,**
   With hearts, and hands, and voices;
   Who wondrous things has done,
   In whom His world rejoices;
   Who, from our mothers' arms,
   Has blessed us on our way
   With countless gifts of love,
   And still is ours today.

2. We thank You then, O God
   That through our life You're near us.
   For joy that fills our hearts
   Which with Your peace restores us.
   Lord, keep us in Your grace
   And guide us when perplexed,
   That we may love Your ways
   In this world and the next.

3. All praise and thanks to God
   The Father now be given,
   The Son, and Him who reigns
   With Them in highest heaven:
   The one, eternal God,
   Whom earth and heaven adore;
   For thus it was, is now,
   And shall be evermore.

176 Latin, 18th cent.
Frederick Oakley 1802-1880
Altered © 1986 Horrobin/Leavers

1. **O Come. all you faithful,**
   Joyful and triumphant,
   O come now, O come now to Bethlehem;
   Come and behold Him,
   Born the King of angels:

   O come, let us adore Him,
   O come, let us adore Him,
   O come, let us adore Him,
   Christ the Lord.

2. True God of true God,
   Light of light eternal,
   He, who abhors not the virgin's womb;
   Son of the Father,
   Begotten not created:
   O come, let us adore Him . . .

3. Sing like the angels,
   Sing in exultation,
   Sing with the citizens of heaven above,
   'Glory to God,
   Glory in the highest':
   O come, let us adore Him . . .

4. Yes, Lord, we greet You,
   Born that happy morning,
   Jesus, to You be glory given;
   Word of the Father,
   Then in flesh appearing:
   O come, let us adore Him . . .

177 from the Latin (thirteenth century)
J.M. Neale 1818-1866 and others
© in this version Jubilate Hymns

1. **O come, O come, Emmanuel**
   And ransom captive Israel
   Who mourns in lonely exile here
   Until the Son of God draws near:
   Rejoice, rejoice!
   Emmanuel shall come to you O Israel.

2. O come, true Branch of Jesse, free
   Your children from this tyranny;
   From depths of hell Your people save,
   To rise victorious from the grave:
   Rejoice, rejoice . . .

3. O come, bright Daybreak, come and cheer
   Our spirits by Your advent here;
   Dispel the long night's lingering gloom
   And pierce the shadows of the tomb:
   Rejoice, rejoice . . .

4. O come, strong Key of David, come
   And open wide our heavenly home;
   Make safe the way that leads on high
   And close the path to misery:
   Rejoice, rejoice . . .

5. O come, O come, great Lord of might
   Who long ago on Sinai's height
   Gave all Your tribes the ancient law
   In cloud and majesty and awe:
   Rejoice, rejoice . . .

178 P. Doddridge 1702-1751
Altered © 1986 Horrobin/Leavers

1. **O happy day that fixed my choice**
   On You, my Saviour and my God!
   Well may this grateful heart rejoice
   And tell of Christ's redeeming blood.

   O happy day, O happy day,
   When Jesus washed my sins away,
   He taught me how to watch and pray,
   And live rejoicing ev'ry day; (Hallelujah!)
   O happy day, O happy day,
   When Jesus washed my sins away.

2. It's done, the great transaction's done!
   I am my Lord's, and He is mine;
   He led me, and I followed on
   Responding to the voice divine.
   O happy day, . . .

3. Now rest, my long-divided heart,
   In Jesus Christ who loves you, rest
   And never from your Lord depart—
   Enriched in Him, by Him possessed!
   O happy day, . . .

4. So God, who heard my solemn vow,
   In daily prayer shall hear my voice
   Till in my final breath I bow
   And bless the day that fixed my choice.
   O happy day, . . .

179

Russian hymn
Tr. © 1953 Stuart K. Hine/Thankyou Music

1. **O Lord my God! when I in awe-some
   wonder**
   Consider all the works Thy hand hath
   made,
   I see the stars, I hear the mighty thunder,
   Thy pow'r throughout the universe
   display'd:

   *Then sings my soul, my Saviour God, to
   Thee,*
   How great Thou art! How great Thou art!
   *Then sings my soul, my Saviour God, to
   Thee,*
   How great Thou art! How great Thou art!

2. When through the woods and forest glades
   I wander
   And hear the birds sing sweetly in the
   trees;
   When I look down from lofty mountain
   grandeur,
   And hear the brook, and feel the gentle
   breeze;
   Then sings my soul, . . .

3. And when I think that God His Son not
   sparing,
   Sent Him to die— I scarce can take it in.
   That on the cross my burden gladly
   bearing,
   He bled and died to take away my sin:
   Then sings my soul, . . .

4. When Christ shall come with shout of
   acclamation
   And take me home— what joy shall fill my
   heart!
   Then shall I bow in humble adoration
   And there proclaim, my God, how great
   Thou art!
   Then sings my soul, . . .

180

Copyright control

Oh! Oh! Oh! how good is the Lord.
Oh! Oh! Oh! how good is the Lord.
Oh! Oh! Oh! how good is the Lord.
I never will forget what He has done for
me.

1. He gives me salvation, how good is the
   Lord.
   He gives me salvation, how good is the
   Lord.
   He gives me salvation, how good is the
   Lord.
   I never will forget what He has done for
   me.
   Oh! Oh! Oh! . . .

2. He gives me His blessings . . .
   Oh! Oh! Oh! . . .

3. He gives me His Spirit . . .
   Oh! Oh! Oh! . . .

4. He gives me His healing . . .
   Oh! Oh! Oh! . . .

5. He gives me His glory . . .
   Oh! Oh! Oh! . . .

Other suitable verses may be added.

181

W. R. Newell

Oh, the love that drew salvation's plan!
Oh, the grace that brought it down to man!
Oh, the mighty gulf that God did span at
   Calvary!
Mercy there was great, and grace was free;
Pardon there was multiplied to me;
There my burdened soul found liberty, at
   Calvary.

182

Phillips Brooks 1835-1893

1. **O little town of Bethlehem,**
   How still we see you lie!
   Above your deep and dreamless sleep
   The silent stars go by:
   Yet in your dark streets shining
   Is everlasting Light;
   The hopes and fears of all the years
   Are met in you tonight.

2. For Christ is born of Mary;
   And, gathered all above
   While mortals sleep, the angels keep
   Their watch of wondering love.
   O morning stars, together
   Proclaim the holy birth,
   And praises sing to God the King,
   And peace to men on earth.

3. How silently, how silently,
   The wondrous gift is given!
   So God imparts to human hearts
   The blessings of His heaven.
   No ear may hear His coming;
   But in this world of sin,
   Where meek souls will receive Him, still
   The dear Christ enters in.

4. O holy child of Bethlehem,
   Descend to us, we pray;
   Cast out our sin, and enter in;
   Be born in us today.
   We hear the Christmas angels
   The great glad tidings tell;
   O come to us, abide with us,
   Our Lord Immanuel.

183

A. W. Edsor
© Kingsway Publications Ltd
administered by Thankyou Music

On Calvary's tree He died for me,
That I His love might know;
To set me free He died for me
That's why I love Him so.

184

1. **Oh, the Lord looked down from his window in the sky,**
   Said: 'I created man, but I can't remember why!
   Nothing but fighting since creation day.
   I'll send a little water and wash them all away.'
   Oh, the Lord came down and looked around a spell.
   There was Mr Noah behaving mighty well.
   And that is the reason the Scriptures record
   Noah found grace in the eyes of the Lord.

   Noah found grace in the eyes of the Lord,
   Noah found grace in the eyes of the Lord,
   Noah found grace in the eyes of the Lord,
   And he left him high and dry.

2. The Lord said: 'Noah, there's going to be a flood,
   There's going to be some water, there's going to be some mud,
   So, take off your hat, Noah, take off your coat,
   Get Shem, Ham and Japheth and build yourself a boat.'
   Noah said: 'Lord, I don't believe I could.'
   The Lord said: 'Noah, get yourself some wood.
   You never know what you can do till you try.
   Build it fifty cubits wide and thirty cubits high.'
   Noah found grace . . .

3. Noah said: 'There she is, there she is, Lord!'
   The Lord said: 'Noah, it's time to get aboard.
   Take of each creature a he and a she,
   And of course take Mrs Noah and the whole family.'
   Noah said: 'Lord, it's getting mighty dark.'
   The Lord said: 'Noah, get those creatures in the ark.'
   Noah said: 'Lord, it's beginning to pour.'
   The Lord said: 'Noah, hurry up and close the door.'
   Noah found grace . . .

4. The ark rose up on the bosom of the deep.
   After forty days Mr Noah took a peep.
   He said: 'We're not moving, Lord, where are we at?'
   The Lord said: 'You're sitting right on Mount Ararat.'
   Noah said: 'Lord, it's getting nice and dry.'
   The Lord said: 'Noah, see my rainbow in the sky.
   Take all your creatures and people the earth,
   And be sure that you're not more trouble than you're worth.'
   Noah found grace . . .

185

Cecil Frances Alexander 1823-1895
alt © Horrobin & Leavers

1. **Once in royal David's city,**
   Stood a lowly cattle shed,
   Where a mother laid her Baby,
   In a manger for His bed.
   Mary was that mother mild,
   Jesus Christ her little child.

2. He came down to earth from heaven,
   Who is God and Lord of all,
   And His shelter was a stable,
   And His cradle was a stall:
   With the poor and mean and lowly
   Lived on earth our Saviour holy.

3. And through all his wondrous childhood
   He would honour and obey,
   Love and watch the lowly mother,
   In whose gentle arms He lay.
   Christian children all should be,
   Kind, obedient, good as He.

4. For He is our childhood's pattern:
   Day by day like us He grew;
   He was little, weak, and helpless;
   Tears and smiles like us He knew:
   And He feels for all our sadness,
   And He shares in all our gladness.

5. And our eyes at last shall see Him
   Through His own redeeming love;
   For that Child, so dear and gentle,
   Is our Lord in heaven above;
   And He leads His children on
   To the place where He is gone.

6. Not in that poor, lowly stable,
   With the oxen standing by,
   We shall see Him, but in heaven,
   Set at God's right hand on high;
   There His children gather round
   Bright like stars, with glory crowned.

186

Charles Coffin 1676-1749
John Chandler 1806-1876, altd.
Altered © 1986 Horrobin/Leavers

1. **On Jordan's bank the Baptist's cry**
   Announces that the Lord is nigh;
   Come then and listen for he brings
   Glad tidings from the King of kings.

2. Then cleansed be every heart from sin;
   Make straight the way for God within;
   Prepare we in our hearts a home,
   Where such a mighty guest may come.

3. For You are our salvation, Lord,
   Our refuge and our great reward;
   Without Your grace we waste away,
   Like flowers that wither and decay.

4. To Him who left the throne of heaven
   To save mankind, all praise be given;
   To God the Father, voices raise,
   And Holy Spirit, let us praise.

187

J. Wilbur Chapman
© Alexander Copyright Trust

1. **One day when heaven was filled with His praises,**
   One day when sin was as black as could be,
   Jesus came down to be born of a virgin,
   Lived among men, my example is He!

   Living, He lov'd me; dying, He saved me;
   Buried, He carried my sins far away,
   Rising, He justified freely for ever:
   One day He's coming O glorious day.

2. One day they led Him up Calvary's mountain,
   One day they nailed Him to die on the tree;
   Suffering anguish, despis'd and rejected;
   Bearing our sins, my Redeemer is He!
   Living, He lov'd me . . .

3. One day they left Him alone in the garden,
   One day He rested, from suffering free;
   Angels came down o'er His tomb to keep vigil;
   Hope of the hopeless my Saviour is He!
   Living, He lov'd me . . .

4. One day the grave could conceal Him no longer,
   One day the stone rolled away from the door;
   Then He arose, over death He had conquer'd;
   Now is ascended, my Lord evermore!
   Living, He lov'd me . . .

5. One day the trumpet will sound for His coming,
   One day the skies with His glory will shine;
   Wonderful day my beloved ones bringing;
   Glorious Saviour, this Jesus is mine!
   Living, He lov'd me . . .

188

Sydney Carter b. 1915
© Stainer & Bell Ltd.

1. **One more step along the world I go,**
   One more step along the world I go,
   From the old things to the new
   Keep me travelling along with You.

   And it's from the old I travel to the new,
   Keep me travelling along with You.

2. Round the corners of the world I turn,
   More and more about the world I learn.
   And the new things that I see
   You'll be looking at along with me.
   And it's from the old . . .

3. As I travel through the bad and good
   Keep me travelling the way I should.
   Where I see no way to go
   You'll be telling me the way, I know.
   And it's from the old . . .

4. Give me courage when the world is rough,
   Keep me loving though the world is tough.
   Leap and sing in all I do,
   Keep me travelling along with You.
   And it's from the old . . .

5. You are older than the world can be
   You are younger than the life in me.
   Ever old and ever new,
   Keep me travelling along with You.
   And its from the old . . .

189

© 1974-1975 Celebration/Thankyou Music

One, two, three, Jesus loves me.
One, two, Jesus loves you

1. Three, four, He loves you more
   Than you've ever been loved before.
   One, two, three, . . .

2. Five, six, seven, we're going to heav'n.
   Eight, nine, it's truly divine.
   One, two, three, . . .

3. Nine, ten, its time to end;
   But instead we'll sing it again
   (There's no time to sing it again).
   One, two, three, . . .

190

Only a boy called David,
Only a rippling brook;
Only a boy called David,
Five little stones he took.
Then, one little stone went in the sling,
And the sling went round and round,
One little stone went in the sling,
And the sling went round and round,
Round and round, and round and round,
And round and round and round;
One little stone went up, up, up!
And the giant came tumbling down.

191

1. **Our eyes have seen the glory of our
   Saviour, Christ the Lord;**
   He's seated at His Father's side in love and
   full accord;
   From there upon the sons of men His Spirit
   is outpoured,
   All hail, ascended King!

   Glory, glory, hallelujah,
   Glory, glory, hallelujah,
   Glory, glory, hallelujah,
   All hail, ascended King!

2. He came to earth at Christmas and was
   made a man like us;
   He taught, He Healed, He suffered— and
   they nailed Him to the cross;
   He rose again on Easter Day— our Lord
   victorious,
   All hail, ascended King!
   Glory, glory, . . .

3. The good news of His kingdom must be
   preached to every shore,
   The news of peace and pardon, and the end
   of strife and war;
   The secret of His kingdom is to serve Him
   evermore,
   All hail, ascended King!
   Glory, glory, . . .

4. His kingdom is a family of men of every
   race,
   They live their lives in harmony, enabled
   by His grace;
   They follow His example till they see Him
   face to face,
   All hail, ascended King!
   Glory, glory, . . .

192

1. **Our Father who is in heaven,**
   Hallowed be Your Name,
   Your Kingdom come, Your will be done,
   Hallowed be Your Name.

2. On earth as it is in heaven,
   Hallowed be Your Name,
   Give us this day our daily bread,
   Hallowed be Your Name.

3. Forgive us all our trespasses,
   Hallowed be Your Name,
   As we forgive those who trespass against us,
   Hallowed be Your Name.

4. And lead us not into temptation,
   Hallowed be Your Name,
   But deliver us from all that is evil,
   Hallowed be Your Name.

5. For Yours is the Kingdom, the Power and
   the Glory,
   Hallowed be Your Name,
   For ever and for ever and ever
   Hallowed be Your Name.

6. Amen, Amen, it shall be so,
   Hallowed be Your Name,
   Amen, Amen, it shall be so,
   Hallowed be Your Name.

193

1. **Our harvest day is over for yet another year.**
   The gifts we've brought to Jesus are now
   before us here.
   Before we go, again we raise our thanks to
   God above
   For all that He provides us with from His
   great hand of love.

2. We thank God for providing fresh air for us
   to breathe.
   Thirst-quenching water, also, to us He does
   bequeath.
   Fresh fruit and daily bread as well are gifts
   from God above,
   Tinned foods, and eggs, and poultry come
   from our great God of love.

3. Our clothes and health come also from
   God's all-gracious hand;
   Our happiness is something which He
   again has planned.
   But something more important still comes
   to us through God's love—
   Eternal life through His dear Son; all praise
   to God above!
   All praise to God above!

194

O sinner man, where will you run to?
O sinner man, where will you run to?
O sinner man, where will you run to,
All on that day?

1. Run to the rocks, rocks won't you hide me?
   Run to the rocks, rocks won't you hide me?
   Run to the rocks, rocks won't you hide me,
   All on that day?
       O sinner man . . .

2. Run to the sea, sea is a-boiling,
   Run to the sea, sea is a-boiling,
   Run to the sea, sea is a-boiling,
   All on that day.
       O sinner man . . .

3. Run to the Lord, Lord won't you hide me?
   Run to the Lord, Lord won't you hide me?
   Run to the Lord, Lord won't you hide me,
   All on that day?
       O sinner man . . .

4. O sinner man, should bin a-praying
   O sinner man, should bin a-praying
   O sinner man, should bin a-praying
   All on that day.
       O sinner man . . .

195

1. O when the saints go marching in,
   O when the saints go marching in;
   O Lord, I want to be among the number
   When the saints go marching in!

2. O when they crown Him Lord of all,
   O when they crown Him Lord of all;
   O Lord, I want to be among the number
   When they crown Him Lord of all.

3. O when all knees bow at His name,
   O when all knees bow at His name,
   O Lord, I want to be among the number
   When all knees bow at His name.

4. O when they sing the Saviour's praise,
   O when they sing the Saviour's praise,
   O Lord, I want to be among the number
   When they sing the Saviour's praise.

5. O when the saints go marching in,
   O when the saints go marching in;
   O Lord, I want to be among the number
   When the saints go marching in!

196

Graham Kendrick
© 1985 Thankyou Music

1. **Peace, I give to you, I give to you my peace.**
   Peace, I give to you, I give to you my peace.

   Let it flow to one another, let it flow, let it flow.
   Let it flow to one another, let it flow, let it flow.

2. Love I give to you, I give you my love.
   Love I give to you, I give you my love.
       Let it flow . . .

3. Hope I give to you, I give you my hope.
   Hope I give to you, I give you my hope.
       Let it flow . . .

4. Joy I give to you, I give you my joy.
   Joy I give to you, I give you my joy.
       Let it flow . . .

197

1. **Peter and James and John in a sailboat,**
   (3 times)
   Out on the beautiful sea.

2. They fished all night but they caught nothing, *(3 times)*
   Out on the beautiful sea.

3. Along came Jesus walking on the water, *(3 times)*
   Out on the beautiful sea.

4. He said 'Throw your nets over on the other side', *(3 times)*
   Out on the beautiful sea.

5. The nets were filled with great big fishes, *(3 times)*
   Out on the beautiful sea.

6. The lesson of this story is listen to the Lord, *(3 times)*
   Wherever you may be.

198

Peter and John went to pray,
They met a lame man on the way.
He asked for alms and held out his palms,
And this is what Peter did say:
'Silver and Gold have I none,
But such as I have I give you,
In the name of Jesus Christ of Nazareth,
Rise up and walk!'
He went walking and leaping and praising
  God,
Walking and leaping and praising God.
'In the name of Jesus Christ of Nazareth,
Rise up and walk.'

199

Jimmy Owens
© 1972 Lexicon Music USA/United Nations Music
Publishing/Boosey & Hawkes Ltd

Praise God from whom all blessings flow;
Praise Him all creatures here below.
Praise Him above you heavenly hosts;
Praise Father, Son, and Holy Ghost.

200

J. Kennett
© 1981 Thankyou Music

**Praise Him on the trumpet, the psaltery and
  harp**
Praise Him on the timbrel and the dance,
Praise Him with stringed instruments too.
Praise Him on the loud cymbals
Praise Him on the loud cymbals
Let ev'rything that has breath praise the
  Lord.
Hallelujah, praise the Lord,
Hallelujah, praise the Lord,
Let ev'rything that has breath praise the
  Lord.

201

1. **Praise Him, praise Him, all you little
  children,**
  God is love, God is love.
  Praise Him, praise Him, all you little
    children,
  God is love, God is love.

2. Love Him, love Him, all you little children,
  God is love, God is love.
  Love Him, love Him, all you little children,
  God is love, God is love.

3. Thank Him, thank Him, all you little
    children,
  God is love, God is love.
  Thank Him, thank Him, all you little
    children,
  God is love, God is love.

202

1. **Praise Him, praise Him,**
  Praise Him in the morning,
  Praise Him in the noontime,
  Praise Him, praise Him,
  Praise Him as the sun goes down.

2. Thank Him . . . *etc.*

3. Love Him . . . *etc.*

4. Serve Him . . . *etc.*

203

Frances van Alstyne 1820-1915
Altered © 1986 Horrobin/Leavers

1. **Praise Him! praise Him! Jesus, our blessèd
    Redeemer!**
  Sing, O earth − His wonderful love
    proclaim!
  Hail Him! hail Him! highest archangels in
    glory;
  Strength and honour give to His holy name!
  Like a shepherd, Jesus will guard His
    children,
  In His arms He carries them all day long.

  *Praise Him! praise Him! tell of His excellent
    greatness;
  Praise Him! praise Him ever in joyful song!*

2. Praise Him! praise Him! Jesus, our blessèd
    Redeemer!
  For our sins He suffered, and bled, and
    died;
  He − our rock, our hope of eternal
    salvation,
  Hail Him! hail Him! Jesus, the crucified!
  Sound His praises − Jesus who bore our
    sorrows,
  Love unbounded, wonderful, deep and
    strong.
    Praise Him! praise Him! . . .

3. Praise Him! praise Him! Jesus, our blessèd
    Redeemer!
  All in heaven let their hosannas ring!
  Jesus, Saviour, reigning for ever and ever:
  Crown Him! crown Him! prophet, and
    priest, and king!
  Christ is coming, over the world victorious,
  Power and glory unto the Lord belong.
    Praise Him! praise Him! . . .

204
H.F. Lyte 1793-1847
Altered © 1986 Horrobin/Leavers

1. **Praise, my soul, the King of heaven;**
   To His feet your worship bring;
   Ransomed, healed, restored, forgiven,
   We do now His praises sing.
   Praise Him! Praise Him! Praise Him! Praise
      Him!
   Praise the everlasting King.

2. Praise Him for His grace and favour
   To our fathers in distress;
   Praise Him, still the same for ever,
   Merciful, He waits to bless.
   Praise Him! Praise Him! Praise Him! Praise
      Him!
   Glorious in His faithfulness.

3. Father-like He loves and spares us;
   Well our weaknesses He knows;
   In His hands He gently bears us,
   Rescues us from all our foes;
   Praise Him! Praise Him! Praise Him! Praise
      Him!
   Widely as His mercy flows.

4. Angels, help us to adore Him!
   You behold Him face to face;
   Sun and moon, bow down before Him;
   Dwellers all in time and space.
   Praise Him! Praise Him! Praise Him! Praise
      Him!
   Praise with us the God of grace.

205
Estelle White
© Mayhew McCrimmon

**Praise to the Lord our God, let us sing
   together,**
Lifting our hearts and our voices to sing
   with
Joy and gladness.
Come along, along, along, and sing with
   praise.

206
Gene MacLellan
© 1970 EMI Publishing
International Music Publishing

1. **Put your hand in the hand of the man who
      stilled the water.**
   Put your hand in the hand of the man who
      calmed the sea.
   Take a look at yourself and you can look at
      others diff'rently,
   By puttin' your hand in the hand of the man
      from Galilee.

2. Ev'rytime I look into the Holy Book I want to
      tremble.
   When I read about the part where a
      carpenter cleared the temple.
   For the buyers and the sellers were no
      diff'rent fellas than what I profess to
      be,
   And it causes me pain to know we're not
      the people we should be.

3. Put your hand in the hand of the man who
      stilled the water.
   Put your hand in the hand of the man who
      calmed the sea.
   Take a look at yourself and you can look at
      others diff'rently,
   By puttin' your hand in the hand of the man
      from Galilee.

207
P Dearmer 1867-1936

1. **Remember all the people**
   Who live in far off lands,
   In strange and lovely cities,
   Or roam the desert sands,
   Or farm the mountain pastures,
   Or till the endless plains
   Where children wade through rice fields
   And watch the camel trains:

2. Some work in sultry forests
   Where apes swing to and fro,
   Some fish in mighty rivers,
   Some hunt across the snow.
   Remember all God's children
   Who yet have never heard
   The truth that comes from Jesus,
   The glory of His Word.

3. God bless the men and women
   Who serve Him oversea;
   God raise up more to help them
   To set the nations free,
   Till all the distant people
   In every foreign place
   Shall understand His Kingdom
   And come into His grace.

208
Phil. 4:4, Copyright Control

**Rejoice in the Lord always, and again I say
   rejoice!**
Rejoice in the Lord always, and again I say
   rejoice!
Rejoice, rejoice, and again I say rejoice!
Rejoice, rejoice, and again I say rejoice!

209
H. Milman 1791-1868
© in this version Jubilate Hymns

1. **Ride on, ride on in majesty**
   As all the crowds 'Hosanna!' cry:
   Through waving branches slowly ride,
   O Saviour, to be crucified.

2. Ride on, ride on in majesty,
   In lowly pomp ride on to die:
   O Christ, your triumph now begin
   With captured death, and conquered sin!

3. Ride on, ride on in majesty—
   The angel armies of the sky
   Look down with sad and wondering eyes
   To see the approaching sacrifice.

4. Ride on, ride on in majesty,
   The last and fiercest foe defy:
   The Father on his sapphire throne
   Awaits his own anointed Son.

5. Ride on, ride on in majesty,
   In lowly pomp ride on to die:
   Bow your meek head to mortal pain,
   Then take, O God, your power and reign!

210

Rise, and shine, and give God his glory,
glory.
Rise, and shine, and give God his glory,
glory.
Rise, and shine, and give God his glory,
glory,
Children of the Lord.

1. The Lord said to Noah: 'There's gonna be a
   floody, floody.'
   Lord said to Noah: 'There's gonna be a
   floody, floody.
   Get those children out of the muddy,
   muddy,
   Children of the Lord.'
   Rise, and shine, . . .

2. The Lord told Noah to build him an arky,
   arky,
   The Lord told Noah to build him an arky,
   arky,
   Build it out of gopher barky, barky,
   Children of the Lord.
   Rise, and shine, . . .

3. The animals, the animals, they came on, by
   twosies, twosies,
   The animals, the animals, they came on, by
   twosies, twosies,
   Elephants and kangaroosies, 'roosies,
   Children of the Lord.
   Rise, and shine, . . .

4. It rained and poured for forty daysies,
   daysies,
   It rained and poured for forty daysies,
   daysies,
   Almost drove those animals crazies,
   crazies,
   Children of the Lord.
   Rise, and shine, . . .

5. The sun came out and dried up the landy,
   landy
   The sun came out and dried up the landy,
   landy
   Everything was fine and dandy, dandy,
   Children of the Lord.
   Rise, and shine, . . .

211
Sydney Carter b. 1915
© Stainer & Bell Ltd

1. **Said Judas to Mary, 'Now what will you do**
   With your ointment so rich and so rare?'
   I'll pour it all over the feet of the Lord
   And I'll wipe it away with my hair,' she
   said.
   I'll wipe it away with my hair.'

2. 'Oh Mary, oh Mary, oh think of the poor—
   This ointment it could have been sold;
   And think of the blankets and think of the
   bread
   You could buy with the silver and gold,' he
   said,
   You could buy with the silver and gold.'

3. 'Tomorrow, tomorrow I'll think of the poor,
   Tomorrow,' she said, 'not today;
   For dearer than all of the poor of the world
   Is my love who is going away,' she said,
   My love who is going away.'

4. Said Jesus to Mary, 'Your love is so deep,
   Today you may do as you will;
   Tomorrow, you say, I am going away,
   But my body I leave with you still,' he said,
   'My body I leave with you still.'

5. 'The poor of the world are my body,' he
   said,
   'To the end of the world they shall be;
   The bread and the blankets you give to the
   poor
   You'll find you have given to me,' he said,
   'You'll find you have given to me.'

6. 'My body will hang on the cross of the
   world
   Tomorrow,' he said, 'and today,
   And Martha and Mary will find me again
   And wash all my sorrow away,' he said,
   'And wash all my sorrow away.'

M. Kaihau © 1928 Charles Begg & Co.Ltd.
Sub published by Keith Prowse Music
by permission E.M.I. Music & I.M.P.

212

**Search me, O God, and know my heart
 today;**
Try me, O Lord, and know my thoughts I
 pray:
See if there be some wicked way in me,
Cleanse me from ev'ry sin and set me free.

213

E. Caswell 1814-1878
Altered © 1986 Horrobin/Leavers

1. **See, amid the winter snow,**
   Born for us on earth below;
   See, the Son of God appears,
   Promised from eternal years:

   Hail, O ever-blessèd morn!
   Hail, redemption's happy dawn!
   Sing through all Jerusalem:
   'Christ is born in Bethlehem!'

2. Low within a manger lies
   He who built the starry skies;
   He who, throned in heaven's height,
   Reigns in power and glorious light:
   Hail, O ever-blessèd morn . . .

3. Say, you humble shepherds, say
   What's your joyful news today?
   Tell us why you left your sheep
   On the lonely mountain steep:
   Hail, O ever-blessèd morn . . .

4. 'As we watched at dead of night,
   All around us shone a light;
   Angels, singing peace on earth,
   Told us of a Saviour's birth.'
   Hail, O ever-blessèd morn . . .

5. Sacred baby, king most dear,
   What a tender love was here,
   Down He came from glory high
   In a manger there to lie.
   Hail, O ever-blessèd morn . . .

6. Holy Saviour, born on earth,
   Teach us by Your lowly birth;
   Grant that we may ever be
   Taught by such humility.
   Hail, O ever-blessèd morn . . .

214

© Michael Perry / Jubilate Hymns

1. **See Him lying on a bed of straw:**
   A draughty stable with an open door;
   Mary cradling the babe she bore—
   The Prince of glory is His name.

O now carry me to Bethlehem
To see the Lord appear to men!
Just as poor as was the stable then,
The Prince of glory when He came.

2. Star of silver, sweep across the skies,
   Show where Jesus in the manger lies;
   Shepherds swiftly from your stupor rise·
   To see the Saviour of the world!
   O now carry . . .

3. Angels, sing the song that you began,
   Bring God's glory to the heart of man;
   Sing that Bethl'em's little baby can
   Be salvation to the soul.
   O now carry . . .

4. Mine are riches, from Your poverty,
   From Your innocence, eternity;
   Mine forgiveness by Your death for me,
   Child of sorrow for my joy.
   O now carry . . .

215

Karen Lafferty
© 1972 Maranatha Music/Word music (UK)

1. **Seek ye first the Kingdom of God,**
   And his righteousness,
   And all these things shall be added unto
    you.
   Allelu, alleluia.
   (Repeat)

2. Man shall not live by bread alone,
   But by every word,
   That proceeds from the mouth of God.
   Allelu, alleluia.

3. Ask and it shall be given unto you,
   Seek and you shall find,
   Knock and the door shall be opened up to
    you.
   Allelu, alleluia.

216

© 1986 Greg Leavers

Saviour of the world, thank you for dying on
the cross.
All praise to You our risen Lord, Hallelujah!
Jesus.

1. In the garden of Gethsemane Jesus knelt
    and prayed,
   For He knew the time was near when He
    would be betrayed.
   God gave Him the strength to cope with all
    that people did to hurt Him;
   Soldiers laughed and forced a crown of
    thorns upon His head.
   Saviour of the world . . .

2. On a cross outside the city they nailed
      Jesus high;
   Innocent, but still He suffered as they
      watched Him die.
   Nothing that the soldiers did could make
      Him lose control, for Jesus
   Knew the time to die then "It is finished",
      was His cry.
      Saviour of the world . . .

3. Three days later by God's pow'r He rose up
      from the dead,
   For the tomb could not hold Jesus it was as
      He'd said;
   Victor over sin and death He conquered
      Satan's power; so let us
   Celebrate that Jesus is alive for ever more.
      Saviour of the world . . .

217 Michael Lehr
         © Stainer & Bell Ltd.

Shalōm, my friend, shalōm, my friend,
Shalōm, shalōm.
Till we meet again, till we meet again,
Shalōm, shalōm.

218 C. Silvester Horne 1865-1914
         Altered © 1986 Horrobin/Leavers

1. **Sing we the King who is coming to reign,**
   Glory to Jesus, the Lamb that was slain.
   Life and salvation His coming shall bring.
   Joy to all those who know Jesus as King.

   Come let us sing: Praise to our King,
   Jesus our King, Jesus our King:
   This is our song, who to Jesus belong:
   Glory to Jesus, to Jesus our King.

2. All men who dwell in His marvellous light,
   Races long severed His love shall unite,
   Justice and truth from His sceptre shall
      spring,
   Wrong shall be ended when Jesus is King.
      Come let us sing . . .

3. All shall be well in His kingdom of peace,
   Freedom and wisdom and love shall not
      cease,
   Foe shall be friend when His triumph we
      sing,
   Sword shall be sickle when Jesus is King.
      Come let us sing . . .

4. Souls shall be saved from the burden of
      sin,
   Doubt shall not darken His witness within,
   Hell has no terrors, and death has no sting;
   Love is victorious when Jesus is King.
      Come let us sing . . .

5. Kingdom of Christ, for Your coming we pray
   Hasten, O Father, the dawn of the day
   When this new song Your creation shall
      sing,
   Satan is conquered and Jesus is King.
      Come let us sing . . .

219 J. Mohr d. 1848
         tr. S.A. Brooke d. 1916

1. **Silent night, holy night!**
   Sleeps the world; hid from sight,
   Mary and Joseph in stable bare
   Watched o'er the Child beloved and fair
   Sleeping in heavenly rest,
   Sleeping in heavenly rest.

2. Silent night, holy night!
   Shepherds first saw the light;
   Heard resounding clear and long,
   Far and near, the angel song:
   'Christ the Redeemer is here',
   'Christ the Redeemer is here'.

3. Silent night, holy night!
   Son of God, O how bright
   Love is smiling from Your face!
   Strikes for us now the hour of grace,
   Saviour, since You are born,
   Saviour, since You are born.

220 Copyright control

1. **Someone's brought a loaf of bread,**
   Someone's brought a loaf of bread,
   Someone's brought a loaf of bread,
   To put on the harvest table.

2. Someone's brought a jar of jam,
   Someone's brought a jar of jam,
   Someone's brought a jar of jam,
   To put on the harvest table.

   Other verses as desired

Last verse:
   Thank You Lord for all your gifts,
   Thank You Lord for all your gifts,
   Thank You Lord for all your gifts,
   To put on the harvest table.

221 Andrae Crouch
         © 1978 Lexicon Music/United Nations Music
         Publishing/Boosey & Hawkes Ltd

1. **Soon and very soon we are going to see
      the King,**
   Soon and very soon we are going to see
      the King,
   Soon and very soon we are going to see
      the King,
   Alleluia, alleluia, we're going to see the
      King!

2. No more cryin' there we are going to see
the King,
No more cryin' there we are going to see
the King,
No more cryin' there we are going to see
the King,
Alleluia, alleluia, we're going to see the
King!

3. No more dyin' there we are going to see
the King,
No more dyin' there we are going to see
the King,
No more dyin' there we are going to see
the King,
Alleluia, alleluia, we're going to see the
King!
Alleluia, alleluia, alleluia, alleluia.

4. Soon and very soon we are going to see
the King,
Soon and very soon we are going to see
the King,
Soon and very soon we are going to see
the King,
Alleluia, alleluia, we're going to see the
King!
Alleluia, alleluia, alleluia, alleluia.

222   © 1935, 1963, Bible Institute of Chicago

Spirit of the living God, fall afresh on me,
Spirit of the living God, fall afresh on me:
Break me, melt me, mould me, fill me;
Spirit of the living God, fall afresh on me.

223   Alfred B Smith & John Peterson
© 1958 Singspiration Inc/United Nations Music
Publishing/Boosey & Hawkes Ltd

**Surely goodness and mercy shall follow
me**
All the days, all the days of my life;
Surely goodness and mercy shall follow
me
All the days, all the days of my life;
And I shall dwell in the house of the Lord
forever,
And I shall feast at the table spread for me;
Surely goodness and mercy shall follow
me
All the days, all the days of my life.

224   © 1986 Andy Silver

Stand up and bless the Lord your God,
Stand up and bless the Lord.
His name is exalted above all names,
Stand up and bless the Lord.
For our God is good to us,
Always ready to forgive,

He is gracious and merciful.
Slow to anger and very kind,
So, stand up and bless the Lord your God,
Stand up and bless the Lord.
So, stand up and bless the Lord your God,
Stand up.

225   Roger Dyer
© 1970 High-Fye Music Ltd.

*Stand up, clap hands, shout thank you,
Lord,*
Thank you for the world I'm in.
Stand up, clap hands, shout thank you, Lord,
For happiness and peace within.

1. I look around and the sun's in the sky,
I look around and then I think oh my!
The world is such a wonderful place,
And all because of the Good Lord's grace:
Stand up, clap hands . . .

2. I look around and the creatures I see,
I look around and it amazes me
That every fox and bird and hare
Must fit in a special place somewhere:
Stand up, clap hands . . .

3. I look around at all the joy I've had,
I look around and then it makes me glad
That I can offer thanks and praise
To Him who guides me through my days:
Stand up, clap hands . . .

226   G. Duffield 1818-1888
© in this version Jubilate Hymns

1. **Stand up, stand up for Jesus,**
You soldiers of the cross!
Lift high His royal banner,
It must not suffer loss:
From victory unto victory
His army He shall lead
Till evil is defeated
And Christ is Lord indeed.

2. Stand up, stand up for Jesus!
The trumpet-call obey;
Then join the mighty conflict
In this His glorious day:
Be strong in faith and serve Him
Against unnumbered foes;
Let courage rise with danger,
And strength to strength oppose.

3. Stand up, stand up for Jesus!
Stand in His power alone,
For human might will fail you—
You dare not trust your own:
Put on the gospel armour,
Keep watch with constant prayer;
Where duty calls or danger
Be never failing there.

4. Stand up, stand up for Jesus!
   The fight will not be long;
   This day the noise of battle,
   The next the victor's song:
   To everyone who conquers,
   A crown of life shall be;
   We, with the king of glory,
   Shall reign eternally.

227

Arabella C. Hankey 1834-1911, altd.

1. **Tell me the old, old story**
   Of unseen things above,
   Of Jesus and His glory,
   Of Jesus and His love.
   Tell me the story simply,
   As to a little child,
   For I am weak and weary,
   And helpless and defiled.

   Tell me the old, old story,
   Tell me the old, old story,
   Tell me the old, old story,
   Of Jesus and His love.

2. Tell me the story slowly,
   That I may take it in—
   That wonderful redemption,
   God's remedy for sin.
   Tell me the story often,
   For I forget so soon:
   The early dew of morning
   Has passed away at noon.
      Tell me the old, old story . . .

3. Tell me the story softly,
   With earnest tones and grave;
   Remember! I'm the sinner
   Whom Jesus came to save.
   Tell me the story always,
   If you would really be,
   In any time of trouble,
   A comforter to me.
      Tell me the old, old story . . .

4. Tell me the same old story,
   When you have cause to fear
   That this world's empty glory
   Is costing me too dear.
   Yes, and when that world's glory
   Is dawning on my soul,
   Tell me the old, old story;
   'Christ Jesus makes you whole.'
      Tell me the old, old story . . .

228

W.H. Parker 1845-1929, altd.
v.6 by Hugh Martin b. 1890
Altered © 1986 Horrobin/Leavers

1. **Tell me the stories of Jesus**
   I love to hear;
   Things I would ask Him to tell me
   If He were here;
   Scenes by the wayside,
   Tales of the sea,
   Stories of Jesus,
   Tell them to me.

2. First let me hear how the children
   Stood round His knee;
   That I may know of His blessing
   Resting on me;
   Words full of kindness,
   Deeds full of grace,
   Signs of the love found
   In Jesus' face.

3. Tell me in words full of wonder,
   How rolled the sea,
   Tossing the boat in a tempest
   On Galilee
   Jesus then doing
   His Father's will,
   Ended the storm say'ng
   Peace, peace be still.

4. Into the city I'd follow
   The children's band,
   Waving a branch of the palm-tree
   High in my hand;
   Worshipping Jesus,
   Yes, I would sing
   Loudest Hosannas,
   For He is King.

5. Show me that scene in the garden,
   Of bitter pain;
   And of the cross where my Saviour
   For me was slain;
   And, through the sadness,
   Help me to see
   How Jesus suffered
   For love of me.

6. Gladly I'd hear of His rising
   Out of the grave,
   Living and strong and triumphant,
   Mighty to save;
   And how He sends us
   All men to bring
   Stories of Jesus,
   Jesus, their King.

229

1. **Tell out, my soul, the greatness of the Lord;**
Unnumbered blessings give my spirit
  voice;
Tender to me the promise of His Word;
In God my Saviour shall my heart rejoice.

2. Tell out, my soul, the greatness of His
  name!
Make known His might, the deeds His arm
  has done;
His mercy sure, from age to age the same;
His Holy Name — the Lord, the Mighty
  One.

3. Tell out, my soul, the greatness of His
  might!
Powers and dominions lay their glory by.
Proud hearts and stubborn wills are put to
  flight,
The hungry fed, the humble lifted high.

4. Tell out, my soul, the glories of His word!
Firm is His promise, and His mercy sure,
Tell out, my soul, the greatness of the Lord
To children's children and for evermore!

230

1. **Thank You for ev'ry new good morning,**
Thank You for ev'ry fresh new day,
Thank You that I may cast my burdens
Wholly on to You.

2. Thank You for ev'ry friend I have, Lord,
Thank You for ev'ry one I know,
Thank You when I can feel forgiveness
To my greatest foe.

3. Thank You for leisure and employment,
Thank You for ev'ry heartfelt joy,
Thank You for all that makes me happy,
And for melody.

4. Thank You for ev'ry shade and sorrow,
Thank You for comfort in Your Word,
Thank You that I am guided by You
Everywhere I go.

5. Thank You for grace to know Your gospel,
Thank You for all Your Spirit's power,
Thank You for Your unfailing love
Which reaches far and near.

6. Thank You for free and full salvation,
Thank You for grace to hold it fast.
Thank You, O Lord I want to thank You
That I'm free to thank!
Thank You, O Lord I want to thank You
That I'm free to thank!

231

1. **Thank You, thank You, Jesus.**
Thank You, thank You, Jesus.
Thank You, thank You, Jesus, in my heart.
Thank You, thank You, Jesus.
Oh, thank You, thank You, Jesus.
Thank You, thank You, Jesus, in my heart.

2. You can't make me doubt Him.
You can't make me doubt Him.
You can't make me doubt Him in my heart.
You can't make me doubt Him.
Oh, You can't make me doubt Him.
Thank You, thank You, Jesus, in my heart.

3. I can't live without Him.
I can't live without Him.
I can't live without Him in my heart.
I can't live without Him.
Oh, I can't live without Him.
Thank You, thank You, Jesus, in my heart.

4. Glory, hallelujah!
Glory, hallelujah!
Glory, hallelujah, in my heart!
Glory, hallelujah!
Oh, Glory, hallelujah!
Thank You, thank You, Jesus, in my heart.

232

1. **Thank You, Lord, for this fine day,**
Thank You, Lord, for this fine day,
Thank You, Lord, for this fine day,
Right where we are.

   Alleluia, praise the Lord!
   Alleluia, praise the Lord!
   Alleluia, praise the Lord!
   Right where we are.

2. Thank You, Lord, for loving us,
Thank You, Lord, for loving us,
Thank You, Lord, for loving us,
Right where we are.
   Alleluia, . . .

3. Thank You, Lord, for giving us peace,
Thank You, Lord, for giving us peace,
Thank You, Lord, for giving us peace,
Right where we are.
   Alleluia, . . .

4. Thank You, Lord, for setting us free,
Thank You, Lord, for setting us free,
Thank You, Lord, for setting us free,
Right where we are.
   Alleluia, . . .

233

Thank You, God, for sending Jesus;
Thank You, Jesus, that you came;
Holy Spirit, won't you tell us
More about His wondrous name?

234

1. **The best book to read is the Bible,**
   The best book to read is the Bible;
   If you read it ev'ry day
   It will help you on your way,
   Oh, the best book to read is the Bible.

2. The best friend to have is Jesus,
   The best friend to have is Jesus;
   He will hear me when I call:
   He will keep me lest I fall,
   Oh, the best friend to have is Jesus.

3. The best thing to do is to trust Him,
   The best thing to do is to trust Him;
   And if you on Him depend,
   He will keep you to the end;
   Oh, the best thing to do is to trust Him.

235

1. **Thank You Jesus, thank You Jesus**
   Thank You Lord for loving me.
   Thank You Jesus thank You Jesus
   Thank You Lord for loving me.

2. You went to Calvary, there You died for me,
   Thank You Lord for loving me.
   You went to Calvary, there You died for me,
   Thank You Lord for loving me.

3. You rose up from the grave, to me new life
      You gave,
   Thank You Lord for loving me.
   You rose up from the grave, to me new life
      You gave,
   Thank You Lord for loving me.

4. You're coming back again, and we with You
      shall reign,
   Thank You Lord for loving me.
   You're coming back again, and we with You
      shall reign,
   Thank You Lord for loving me.

236 J. Ellerton 1826-1893

1. **The day You gave us, Lord, is ended,**
   The sun is sinking in the west;
   To You our morning hymns ascended,
   Your praise shall sanctify our rest.

2. We thank You that Your church, unsleeping
   While earth rolls onward into light,
   Through all the world her watch is keeping
   And rests not now by day or night.

3. As to each continent and island
   The dawn proclaims another day,
   The voice of prayer is never silent,
   Nor dies the sound of praise away.

4. The sun that bids us rest is waking
   Your church beneath the western sky;
   Fresh voices hour by hour are making
   Your mighty deeds resound on high.

5. So be it, Lord: Your throne shall never,
   Like earth's proud empires, pass away;
   Your kingdom stands, and grows for ever,
   Until there dawns that glorious day.

237

1. **The fields are white unto harvest time,**
   Look up and see!
   The fields are white unto harvest time,
   Look up and see:

   Pray to the Lord of the harvest,
   Christ says pray.
   Pray to the Lord for the workers
   Which we need in this day.

2. The harvest truly is fit to reap
   But workers few,
   The harvest truly is fit to reap
   But workers few:
      Pray to the Lord . . .

3. Who else will 'go into all the world'
   To preach the Word?
   Who else will 'go into all the world'
   To preach the Word?
      Pray to the Lord . . .

4. The Lord's return may be very soon,
   The time is short!
   The Lord's return may be very soon,
   The time is short:
      Pray to the Lord . . .

238 unknown (c. seventeenth century)

1. **The first nowell the angel did say**
   Was to Bethlehem's shepherds in fields as
      they lay;
   In fields where they lay keeping their sheep
   On a cold winter's night that was so deep:

   Nowell, nowell, nowell, nowell,
   Born is the king of Israel!

2. Then wise men from a country far
   Looked up and saw a guiding star;
   They travelled on by night and day
   To reach the place where Jesus lay:
   Nowell, nowell, . . .

3. At Bethlehem they entered in,
   On bended knee they worshipped Him;
   They offered there in his presence
   Their gold and myrrh and frankincense:
   Nowell, nowell, . . .

4. Then let us all with one accord
   Sing praises to our heavenly Lord;
   For Christ has our salvation wrought
   And with His blood mankind has bought:
   Nowell, nowell, . . .

239

Mark Pendergras
© Sparrow Song/Candle Co Music
BMG Music Publishing USA

1. **The greatest thing in all my life is knowing You.**
   The greatest thing in all my life is knowing
   You.
   I want to know You more;
   I want to know You more.
   The greatest thing in all my life is knowing
   You.

2. The greatest thing in all my life is loving
   You.
   The greatest thing in all my life is loving
   You.
   I want to love You more;
   I want to love You more.
   The greatest thing in all my life is loving
   You.

3. The greatest thing in all my life is serving
   You.
   The greatest thing in all my life is serving
   You.
   I want to serve You more;
   I want to serve You more.
   The greatest thing in all my life is serving
   You.

240

Alliene Vale
© 1978 His Eye Music/BMG Music Publishing USA

1. **The joy of the Lord is my strength,**
   The joy of the Lord is my strength,
   The joy of the Lord is my strength,
   The joy of the Lord is my strength.

2. If you want joy, you must sing for it,
   If you want joy, you must sing for it,
   If you want joy, you must sing for it,
   The joy of the Lord is my strength.

3. If you want joy, you must shout for it,
   If you want joy, you must shout for it,
   If you want joy, you must shout for it,
   The joy of the Lord is my strength.

4. If you want joy, you must jump for it,
   If you want joy, you must jump for it,
   If you want joy, you must jump for it,
   The joy of the Lord is my strength.

241

H.W. Baker 1821-1877
© in this version Jubilate Hymns

1. **The King of love my shepherd is,**
   Whose goodness fails me never;
   I nothing lack if I am His
   And He is mine for ever.

2. Where streams of living water flow
   A ransomed soul, He leads me;
   And where the fertile pastures grow,
   With food from heaven feeds me.

3. Perverse and foolish I have strayed,
   But in His love He sought me;
   And on His shoulder gently laid,
   And home, rejoicing, brought me.

4. In death's dark vale I fear no ill
   With You, dear Lord, beside me;
   Your rod and staff my comfort still,
   Your cross before to guide me.

5. You spread a banquet in my sight
   Of love beyond all knowing;
   And O the gladness and delight
   From Your pure chalice flowing!

6. And so through all the length of days
   Your goodness fails me never;
   Good Shepherd, may I sing Your praise
   Within Your house for ever!

242

Cecil J. Allen
© G.F. Allen

The Lord has need of me,
His soldier I will be;
He gave Himself my life to win,
And so I mean to follow Him,
And serve Him faithfully.
So although the fight be fierce and long,
I'll carry on, He makes me strong;
And then one day His face I'll see,
And Oh! the joy when He says to me,
'Well done! My brave Crusader!'

243

Francis Rous 1579-1659
revised for Scottish Psalter, 1650
Altered © 1986 Horrobin/Leavers

1. **The Lord's my shepherd, I'll not want;**
   He makes me down to lie
   In pastures green; He's leading me
   The quiet waters by.

2. My soul He does restore again,
And me to walk does make
Within the paths of righteousness,
E'en for His own name's sake.

3. Yes, though I walk through death's dark vale,
Yet will I fear no ill;
For You are with me, and Your rod
And staff me comfort still.

4. My table You have furnishèd
In presence of my foes;
My head You now with oil anoint,
And my cup overflows.

5. Goodness and mercy all my life
Shall surely follow me;
And in God's house for evermore
My dwelling-place shall be.

244 Copyright control

The Lord is my Shepherd,
I'll trust in Him always.
He leads me by still waters,
I'll trust in Him always.
Always, always, I'll trust in Him always,
Always, always, I'll trust in Him always.

245 Cecil Frances Alexander 1823-1895

1. **There is a green hill far away,**
Outside a city wall,
Where the dear Lord was crucified
Who died to save us all.

2. We may not know, we cannot tell
What pains He had to bear;
But we believe it was for us
He hung and suffered there.

3. He died that we might be forgiven,
He died to make us good,
That we might go at last to heaven
Saved by His precious blood.

4. There was no other good enough
To pay the price of sin;
He only could unlock the gate
Of heaven, and let us in.

5. O dearly, dearly has He loved,
And we must love Him too,
And trust in His redeeming blood,
And try His works to do.

246 J. Gowans
© 1970 Salvationist Publishing & Supplies Ltd.

1. **There are hundreds of sparrows, thousands, millions,**
They're two a penny, far too many there must be;
There are hundreds and thousands, millions of sparrows,
But God knows ev'ry-one and God knows me.

2. There are hundreds of flowers, thousands, millions ,
And flowers fair the meadows wear for all to see;
There are hundreds and thousands, millions of flowers,
But God knows ev'ry-one and God knows me.

3. There are hundreds of planets, thousands, millions,
Way out in space each has a place by God's decree;
There are hundreds and thousands, millions of planets,
But God knows ev'ry-one and God knows me.

4. There are hundreds of children, thousands, millions ,
And yet their names are written on God's memory,
There are hundreds and thousands, millions of children,
But God knows ev'ry-one and God knows me.
But God knows ev'ry-one and God knows me.

247 Copyright control

(all)   **There's a song of exaltation**
      Full of joy and inspiration
      Echoed down through all creation,
      Sing Hallelujah sing,
(boys)   Sing Hallelujah,
(girls)   Sing Hallelujah,
(boys)   Sing Hallelujah,
(girls)   Sing Hallelujah,
(boys)   Sing Hallelujah,
(girls)   Sing Hallelujah,
(all)   Sing Hallelujah sing.

248 E.H. Swinstead
Copyright control

There's a way back to God from the dark paths of sin;
There's a door that is open and you may go in:
At Calvary's cross is where you begin,
When you come as a sinner to Jesus.

249 Copyright control

1. **There's new life in Jesus, Lift up your heart;**
There's new life in Jesus, Lift up your heart;
Lift up your heart, Lift up your heart,
There's new life in Jesus, Lift up your heart.

2. There is healing in His love,
There is healing in His love,
Lift up your heart, Lift up your heart,
There's new life in Jesus, Lift up your heart.

3. There is joy in serving Him,
There is joy in serving Him,
Lift up your heart, Lift up your heart,
There's new life in Jesus, Lift up your heart.

250 Edith McNeill
© 1974, 1975 Celebration/Thankyou Music

The steadfast love of the Lord never ceases;
His mercies never come to an end.
They are new ev'ry morning,
New ev'ry morning,
Great is Your faithfulness, O Lord,
Great is Your faithfulness.

251 © 1959 Boosey & Hawkes Inc.

1. **The Virgin Mary had a baby boy,**
The Virgin Mary had a baby boy,
The Virgin Mary had a baby boy,
And they said that His name was Jesus.

He come from the glory
He come from the glorious kingdom;
He come from the glory
He come from the glorious kingdom;
Oh, yes! believer.
Oh, yes! believer.
He come from the glory
He come from the glorious kingdom.

2. The angels sang when the baby was born,
The angels sang when the baby was born,
The angels sang when the baby was born,
And proclaimed Him the Saviour Jesus.
He come from ...

3. The wise men saw where the baby was born,
The wise men saw where the baby was born,
The wise men saw where the baby was born,
And they saw that His name was Jesus.
He come from ...

252 Copyright control

1. **The wise man built his house upon the rock.**
The wise man built his house upon the rock.
The wise man built his house upon the rock
And the rain came tumbling down.
And the rain came down and the floods came up,
The rain came down and the floods came up,
The rain came down and the floods came up,
And the house on the rock stood firm.

2. The foolish man built his house upon the sand.
The foolish man built his house upon the sand.
The foolish man built his house upon the sand
And the rain came tumbling down.
And the rain came down and the floods came up,
The rain came down and the floods came up,
The rain came down and the floods came up,
And the house on the sand fell flat.

253 Book of Praise for Children, 1881, altd.

1. **The wise may bring their learning,**
The rich may bring their wealth,
And some may bring their greatness,
And some their strength and health:
We too would bring our treasures
To offer to the King;
We have no wealth or learning,
What gifts then shall we bring?

2. We'll bring the many duties
   We have to do each day;
   We'll try our best to please Him,
   At home, at school, at play:
   And better are these treasures
   To offer to the King;
   Than richest gifts without them;
   Yet these we all may bring.

3. We'll bring Him hearts that love Him,
   We'll bring Him thankful praise,
   And lives for ever striving
   To follow in His ways:
   And these shall be the treasures
   We offer to the King,
   And these are gifts that ever
   Our grateful hearts may bring.

254 Doreen Newport
© Stainer & Bell Ltd.

1. **Think of a world without any flowers,**
   Think of a world without any trees,
   Think of a sky without any sunshine,
   Think of the air without any breeze.
   We thank You, Lord, for flow'rs and trees
         and sunshine,
   We thank You, Lord, and praise Your Holy
         Name.

2. Think of a world without any animals,
   Think of a field without any herd,
   Think of a stream without any fishes,
   Think of a dawn without any bird.
   We thank You, Lord, for all Your living
         creatures,
   We thank You, Lord, and praise Your Holy
         Name.

3. Think of a world without any people,
   Think of a street with no one living there,
   Think of a town without any houses,
   No one to love and nobody to care.
   We thank You, Lord, for families and
         friendships,
   We thank You, Lord, and praise Your Holy
         Name.

255 Les Garrett
© 1980 Scripture in Song/
Thankyou Music

1. **This is the day,**
   This is the day that the Lord has made,
   That the Lord has made.
   We will rejoice,
   We will rejoice and be glad in it
   And be glad in it.
   This is the day that the Lord has made
   We will rejoice and be glad in it.
   This is the day,
   This is the day that the Lord has made.

2. This is the day,
   This is the day when He rose again,
   When He rose again,
   We will rejoice,
   We will rejoice and be glad in it,
   And be glad in it.
   This is the day when He rose again.
   We will rejoice and be glad in it.
   This is the day,
   This is the day when He rose again.

3. This is the day,
   This is the day when the Spirit came,
   When the Spirit came,
   We will rejoice,
   We will rejoice and be glad in it,
   And be glad in it.
   This is the day when the Spirit came.
   We will rejoice and be glad in it.
   This is the day,
   This is the day when the Spirit came.

256 Fred Pratt Green b. 1903
© Stainer & Bell Ltd.

1. **This joyful Eastertide,**
   What need is there for grieving?
   Cast all your care aside
   And be not unbelieving:

   Come, share our Easter joy
   That death could not imprison,
   Nor any power destroy,
   Our Christ, who is arisen,
   Arisen, arisen, arisen!

2. No work for Him is vain,
   No faith in Him mistaken,
   For Easter makes it plain
   His Kingdom is not shaken:
      Come, share our Easter joy . . .

3. Then put your trust in Christ,
   In waking or in sleeping.
   His grace on earth sufficed;
   He'll never quit His keeping:
      Come, share our Easter joy . . .

257 © 1964 R T Bewes / Jubilate Hymns

1. **Though the world has forsaken God,**
   Treads a diff'rent path, lives a diff'rent way,
   I walk the road that the Saviour trod,
   And all may know I live under Jesus' sway:

   They are watching you, marking all you do,
   Hearing the things you say;
   Let them see the Saviour as He shines in
      you,
   Let His pow'r control you ev'ry day.

2. Men will look at the life I lead,
See the side I take, and the things I love;
They judge my Lord by my every deed—
Lord, set my affections on things above:
They are watching you . . .

3. When assailed in temptation's hour,
By besetting sins, by the fear of man,
Then I can know Jesus' mighty power,
And become like Him in His perfect plan:
They are watching you . . .

4. Here on earth people walk in the night;
With no lamp to guide, they are dead in sin;
I know the Lord Who can give them light,
I live, yet not I, but Christ within:
They are watching you . . .

258

*This little light of mine, I'm gonna let it
shine,*
*This little light of mine, I'm gonna let it
shine,*
*This little light of mine, I'm gonna let it
shine,*
Let it shine, let it shine, let it shine.

1. The light that shines is the light of love,
Lights the darkness from above.
It shines on me and it shines on you,
And shows what the power of love can do.
I'm gonna shine my light both far and near,
I'm gonna shine my light both bright and
clear.
Where there's a dark corner in this land
I'm gonna let my little light shine.
This little light of mine . . .

2. On Monday He gave me the gift of love,
Tuesday, peace came from above.
On Wednesday He told me to have more
faith,
On Thursday He gave me a little more
grace.
Friday, He told me just to watch and pray,
Saturday, He told me just what to say.
On Sunday He gave me the power divine
To let my little light shine.
This little light of mine . . .

259 Frances van Alstyne 1820-1915

1. **To God be the glory! Great things He has
done!**
So loved He the world that He gave us His
Son;
Who yielded His life an atonement for sin,
And opened the life gate that all may go in.

*Praise the Lord! Praise the Lord! Let the
earth hear His voice!*
*Praise the Lord! Praise the Lord! Let the
people rejoice!*
*O come to the Father, through Jesus the
Son:*
*And give Him the glory! Great things He
has done!*

2. O perfect redemption, the purchase of
blood!
To every believer the promise of God;
The vilest offender who truly believes,
That moment from Jesus a pardon
receives.
Praise the Lord! . . .

3. Great things He has taught us, great things
He has done,
And great our rejoicing through Jesus the
Son;
But purer, and higher, and greater will be
Our wonder, our rapture, when Jesus we
see.
Praise the Lord! . . .

260

1. **Turn your eyes upon Jesus,**
Look full in His wonderful face;
And the things of earth will grow strangely
dim
In the light of His glory and grace.

2. Keep your eyes upon Jesus,
Let nobody else take His place;
So that hour by hour you will know His
power
Till at last you have run the great race.

261

Twelve men went to spy in Canaan,
Ten were bad, two were good.
What did they see when they spied in Canaan?
Ten were bad, two were good.
Some saw giants tough and tall,
Some saw grapes in clusters fall,
Some saw God was in it all,
Ten were bad, two were good.

262

Two little eyes to look to God,
Two little ears to hear His Word,
Two little feet to walk in His ways,
Two little lips to sing His praise,
Two little hands to do His will,
And one little heart to love Him still.

263

German (15th c) tr Percy Dearmer d 1936

1. **Unto us a Boy is born!**
   King of all creation,
   Came He to a world forlorn
   The Lord of every nation,
   The Lord of every nation.

2. Cradled in a stall was He
   With sleepy cows and asses;
   But the very beasts could see
   That He all men surpasses,
   That He all men surpasses,

3. Herod then with fear was filled:
   'A prince,' he said, 'in Jewry!'
   All the little boys he killed
   At Bethlehem in his fury,
   At Bethlehem in his fury.

4. Now may Mary's Son, who came
   So long ago to love us,
   Lead us all with hearts aflame
   Unto the joys above us,
   Unto the joys above us.

5. Alpha and Omega He!
   Let the organ thunder,
   While the choir with peals of glee
   Doth rend the air asunder!
   Doth rend the air asunder!

264

Fred Kaan
© Stainer & Bell Ltd.

1. **We have a king who rides a donkey,**
   We have a king who rides a donkey,
   We have a king who rides a donkey
   And his name is Jesus.

   Jesus, the king, is risen,
   Jesus, the king, is risen,
   Jesus, the king, is risen
   Early in the morning.

2. Trees are waving a royal welcome,
   Trees are waving a royal welcome,
   Trees are waving a royal welcome
   For the king called Jesus.
   Jesus, the king, is risen . . .

3. We have a king who cares for people,
   We have a king who cares for people,
   We have a king who cares for people
   And his name is Jesus.
   Jesus, the king, is risen . . .

4. What shall we do with our life this morning?
   What shall we do with our life this morning?
   What shall we do with our life this morning?
   Give it up in service!
   Jesus, the king, is risen . . .

265

© 1986 Margaret Westworth

1. **We love to praise You Jesus,**
   We love to tell You
   That You are Lord, that You are Lord.

2. We love to know You Jesus,
   We love to hear You
   Say we are Yours, say we are Yours.

3. We want to thank You Jesus,
   For giving Your life
   So we can live, so we can live.

266

Priscilla Ownes 1829-1907
Altered © 1986 Horrobin/Leavers

1. **We have heard a joyful sound!**
   Jesus saves!
   Spread the gladness all around:
   Jesus saves!
   Words of life for every land,
   Must be sent across the waves;
   Onward! 'tis our Lord's command:
   Jesus saves!

2. Sing above the toils of life:
   Jesus saves!
   He is with us in the strife:
   Jesus saves!
   Sing the truth, He died yet lives,
   Strength'ning me through all my days.
   Sing in triumph! Life He gives:
   Jesus saves!

3. Let the nations hear God's voice:
   Jesus saves!
   So that they can then rejoice:
   Jesus saves!
   Shout salvation full and free
   That ev'ry land may hear God's praise
   This our song of victory:
   Jesus saves!

267

Matthias Claudius 1740-1815
tr. Jane Montgomery Campbell 1817-1878
Altered © 1986 Horrobin/Leavers

1. **We plough the fields and scatter**
   The good seed on the land,
   But it is fed and watered
   By God's almighty hand;
   He sends the snow in winter,
   The warmth to swell the grain,
   The breezes and the sunshine
   And soft refreshing rain.

   All good gifts around us
   Are sent from heaven above,
   Then thank the Lord, O thank the Lord,
   For all His love.

2. He only is the Maker
   Of all things near and far;
   He paints the wayside flower,
   He lights the evening star;
   The wind and waves obey Him,
   By Him the birds are fed;
   Much more to us, His children,
   He gives our daily bread.
       All good gifts . . .

3. We thank You then, O Father,
   For all things bright and good,
   The seed-time and the harvest,
   Our life, our health, our food.
   Accept the gifts we offer
   For all Your love imparts,
   We come now Lord to give you
   Our humble, thankful hearts.
       All good gifts . . .

268

Ed Baggett
© 1974, 1975 Celebration/Thankyou Music

We really want to thank You Lord.
We really want to bless Your name.
Hallelujah! Jesus is our king!
We really want to thank You Lord.
We really want to bless Your name.
Hallelujah! Jesus is our king!

1. We thank You Lord, for Your gift to us,
   Your life so rich beyond compare,
   The gift of Your body here on earth
   Of which we sing and share.
       We really want to thank . . .

2. We thank You Lord, for our life together,
   To live and move in the love of Christ,
   Your tenderness which sets us free
   To serve You with our lives.
       We really want to thank . . .

3. Praise God from whom all blessings flow,
   Praise Him all creatures here below,
   Praise Him above you heavenly host,
   Praise Father, Son and Holy Ghost.
       We really want to thank . . .

269

1. **Were you there when they crucified my
   Lord?**
   Were you there when they crucified my
   Lord?
   Oh! Sometimes it causes me to tremble,
   tremble, tremble;
   Were you there when they crucified my
   Lord?

2. Were you there when they nailed Him to
   the tree?
   Were you there when they nailed Him to
   the tree?
   Oh! Sometimes it causes me to tremble,
   tremble, tremble;
   Were you there when they nailed Him to
   the tree?

3. Were you there when they laid Him in the
   tomb?
   Were you there when they laid Him in the
   tomb?
   Oh! Sometimes it causes me to tremble,
   tremble, tremble;
   Were you there when they laid Him in the
   tomb?

4. Were you there when God raised Him from
   the dead?
   Were you there when God raised Him from
   the dead?
   Oh! Sometimes it causes me to tremble,
   tremble, tremble;
   Were you there when God raised Him from
   the dead?

270

Zilphia Horton, Frank Hamilton
Guy Carawan, Pete Seeger
© 1960, 1963 Ludlow Music
assigned to TRO. Essex Music Ltd.

1. **We shall overcome,**
   We shall overcome,
   We shall overcome some day;
   By faith in Christ I do believe
   We shall overcome some day.

2. The truth will make us free,
   The truth will make us free,
   The truth will make us free some day;
   By faith in Christ I do believe
   We shall overcome some day.

3. The Lord will see us through,
   The Lord will see us through,
   The Lord will see us through some day.
   By faith in Christ I do believe
   We shall overcome some day.

4. We shall live in peace,
   We shall live in peace,
   We shall live in peace some day;
   By faith in Christ I do believe
   We shall overcome some day.

5. We shall overcome,
   We shall overcome,
   We shall overcome some day;
   By faith in Christ I do believe
   We shall overcome some day.

271

J.H. Hopkins Jnr. d. 1891
Altered © 1986 Horrobin/Leavers

1. **We three kings of Orient are;**
   Bearing gifts we travel afar,
   Field and fountain, moor and mountain,
   Following yonder star:

   O star of wonder, star of night,
   Star with royal beauty bright,
   Westward leading, still proceeding,
   Guide us to the perfect light.

2. Born a King on Bethlehem plain,
   Gold I bring, to crown Him again—
   King for ever, ceasing never,
   Over us all to reign:
   O star of wonder, . . .

3. Frankincense for Jesus have I,
   God on earth yet Priest on high;
   Prayer and praising all men raising
   Worship is earth's reply.
   O star of wonder, . . .

4. Myrrh is mine; its bitter perfume
   Tells of His death and Calvary's gloom;
   Sorrowing, sighing, bleeding, dying,
   Sealed in a stone-cold tomb:
   O star of wonder, . . .

5. Glorious now, behold Him arise,
   King, and God, and sacrifice:
   Heaven sings 'Alleluia',
   'Alleluia' the earth replies:
   O star of wonder, . . .

272

Colin Sterne 1862-1926
Altered © 1986 Horrobin/Leavers

1. **We've a story to tell to the nations,**
   That shall turn their hearts to the right,
   A story of truth and sweetness,
   A story of peace and light:

   For the darkness shall turn to dawning,
   And the dawning to noon-day bright,
   And Christ's great kingdom shall come on
        earth,
   The kingdom of love and light.

2. We've a song to be sung to the nations,
   That shall lift their hearts to the Lord;
   A song that shall conquer evil,
   So love will replace the sword:
   For the darkness shall . . .

3. We've a message to give to the nations,
   That the Lord who's reigning above
   Has sent us His Son to save us,
   And show us that God is love:
   For the darkness shall . . .

4. We've a Saviour to show to the nations,
   Who the path of sorrow has trod,
   That all of the world may listen
   And learn of the truth of God:
   For the darkness shall . . .

273

Joseph Scriven 1819-1886
Altered © 1986 Horrobin/Leavers

1. **What a friend we have in Jesus,**
   All our sins and griefs to bear!
   What a privilege to carry
   Everything to God in prayer!
   O what peace we often forfeit,
   O what needless pain we bear—
   All because we do not carry
   Everything to God in prayer!

2. Have we trials and temptations?
   Is there trouble anywhere?
   We should never be discouraged:
   Take it to the Lord in prayer!
   Can we find a friend so faithful,
   Who will all our sorrows share?
   Jesus knows our every weakness—
   Take it to the Lord in prayer!

3. Are we weak and heavy-laden,
   Burdened with a load of care?
   Jesus only is our refuge,
   Take it to the Lord in prayer!
   Do your friends despise, forsake you?
   Take it to the Lord in prayer!
   In His arms He'll take and shield you,
   You will find His comfort there.

274

1. **What a wonderful Saviour is Jesus,**
   What a wonderful Friend is He,
   For He left all the glory of heaven,
   Came to earth to die on Calvary:

   Sing Hosanna! Sing Hosanna!
   Sing Hosanna to the King of kings!
   Sing Hosanna! Sing Hosanna!
   Sing Hosanna to the King.

2. He arose from the grave, Hallelujah,
   And He lives never more to die,
   At the Father's right hand interceding
   He will hear and heed our faintest cry:
   Sing Hosanna! . . .

3. He is coming some day to receive us,
   We'll be caught up to heaven above,
   What a joy it will be to behold Him,
   Sing forever of His grace and love.
   Sing Hosanna! . . .

275

1. **When I needed a neighbour, were you there, were you there?**
   When I needed a neighbour, were you there?

   And the creed and the colour and the name won't matter,
   Were you there?

2. I was hungry and thirsty, were you there, were you there?
   I was hungry and thirsty, were you there?
   And the creed . . .

3. I was cold, I was naked, were you there, were you there?
   I was cold, I was naked, were you there?
   And the creed . . .

4. When I needed a shelter, were you there, were you there?
   When I needed a shelter, were you there?
   And the creed . . .

5. When I needed a healer, were you there, were you there?
   When I needed a healer, were you there?
   And the creed . . .

6. Wherever you travel, I'll be there, I'll be there,
   Wherever you travel, I'll be there,
   And the creed . . .

276

1. **When Israel was in Egypt's land,**
   Let my people go;
   Oppressed so hard they could not stand,
   Let my people go.

   Go down, Moses, way down in Egypt's land;
   Tell old Pharaoh to let my people go.

2. The Lord told Moses what to do,
   Let my people go;
   To lead the children of Israel through,
   Let my people go.
   Go down, Moses . . .

3. Your foes shall not before you stand,
   Let my people go;
   And you'll possess fair Canaan's land,
   Let my people go.
   Go down, Moses . . .

4. O let us from all bondage flee,
   Let my people go;
   And let us all in Christ be free,
   Let my people go.
   Go down, Moses . . .

5. I do believe without a doubt,
   Let my people go;
   That a Christian has a right to shout,
   Let my people go.
   Go down, Moses . . .

277

1. **When I survey the wondrous cross**
   On which the Prince of Glory died,
   My richest gain I count but loss,
   And pour contempt on all my pride.

2. Forbid it, Lord, that I should boast,
   Save in the death of Christ my God:
   All the vain things that charm me most,
   I sacrifice them to His blood.

3. See from His head, His hands, His feet,
   Sorrow and love flow mingled down:
   Did e'er such love and sorrow meet,
   Or thorns compose so rich a crown?

4. Were the whole realm of nature mine,
   That were an offering far too small,
   Love so amazing, so divine,
   Demands my soul, my life, my all.

278

1. **When morning gilds the skies,**
   My heart awakening cries:
   May Jesus Christ be praised!
   Alike at work and prayer
   I know my Lord is there:
   May Jesus Christ be praised!

2. When sadness fills my mind
   My strength in Him I find:
   May Jesus Christ be praised!
   When earthly hopes grows dim
   My comfort is in Him:
   May Jesus Christ be praised!

3. The night becomes as day
   When from the heart we say:
   May Jesus Christ be praised!
   The powers of darkness fear
   When this glad song they hear:
   May Jesus Christ be praised!

4. Be this, while life is mine,
   My canticle divine:
   May Jesus Christ be praised!
   Be this the eternal song
   Through all the ages long:
   May Jesus Christ be praised!

279
Norman J. Clayton
© Norman J. Clayton Pub. Co./Word Music (UK)

When the road is rough and steep,
Fix your eyes upon Jesus,
He alone has pow'r to keep,
Fix your eyes upon Him;
Jesus is a gracious friend,
One on whom you can depend,
He is faithful to the end,
Fix your eyes upon Him.

280 © Timothy Dudley-Smith

1. **When the Lord in glory comes**
   Not the trumpets, not the drums,
   Not the anthem, not the psalm,
   Not the thunder, not the calm,
   Not the shout the heavens raise,
   Not the chorus, not the praise,
   Not the silences sublime,
   Not the sounds of space and time,
   But His voice when He appears
   Shall be music to my ears—
   But His voice when He appears
   Shall be music to my ears.

2. When the Lord is seen again
   Not the glories of His reign,
   Not the lightnings through the storm,
   Not the radiance of His form,
   Not His pomp and power alone,
   Not the splendours of His throne,
   Not His robe and diadems,
   Not the gold and not the gems,
   But His face upon my sight
   Shall be darkness into light—
   But His face upon my sight
   Shall be darkness into light.

3. When the Lord to human eyes
   Shall bestride our narrow skies,
   Not the child of humble birth,
   Not the carpenter of earth,
   Not the man by all denied,
   Not the victim crucified,
   But the God who died to save,
   But the victor of the grave,
   He it is to whom I fall,
   Jesus Christ, my All in all—
   He it is to whom I fall,
   Jesus Christ, my All in all.

281 James M Black 1856-1938

1. **When the trumpet of the Lord shall sound,
   and time shall be no more,**
   And the morning breaks, eternal, bright,
   and fair;

When the saved of earth shall gather over
   on the other shore
And the roll is called up yonder, I'll be
   there.

When the roll is called up yonder,
When the roll is called up yonder,
When the roll is called up yonder,
When the roll is called up yonder, I'll be
   there.

2. On that bright and cloudless morning when
   the dead in Christ shall rise,
   And the glory of his resurrection share;
   When His chosen ones shall gather to their
   home beyond the skies,
   And the roll is called up yonder, I'll be
   there.
   When the roll . . .

3. Let us labour for the Master from the dawn
   till setting sun,
   Let us talk of all His wond'rous love and
   care;
   Then when all of life is over, and our work
   on earth is done,
   And the roll is called up yonder, I'll be
   there.
   When the roll . . .

282 Copyright control

Wherever I am I'll praise him,
Whenever I can I'll praise him;
For his love surrounds me like a sea;
I'll praise the name of Jesus,
Lift up the name of Jesus,
For the name of Jesus lifted me.

283 © 1986 Margaret Westworth

1. **Wherever I am I will praise You Lord,**
   Praise You Lord.
   Wherever I am
   Your Spirit fills my life with song.

2. Whenever I can I will tell You Lord
   I love You.
   Wherever I am
   Your Spirit fills my heart with love.

3. Wherever I go I will serve You Lord,
   Serve You Lord
   Wherever I am
   Your Spirit fills my life with power.

4. Whatever I do I will need You Lord,
   Need You Lord.
   Wherever I am
   Your Spirit lives Your life through me.

284

Graham Kendrick
© 1986 Thankyou Music

1. **Whether you're one or whether you're two**
   Or three or four or five,
   Six or seven or eight or nine
   It's good to be alive.
   It really doesn't matter how old you are,
   Jesus loves you whoever you are.

   *La la la la la la la la la
   Jesus loves us all.
   La la la la la la la la la
   Jesus loves us all.*

2. Whether you're big or whether you're small
   Or somewhere in between,
   First in the class or middle or last
   We're all the same to Him.
   It really doesn't matter how clever you are,
   Jesus loves you whoever you are.
     La la la la la la . . .

285

Nahum Tate 1652-1715

1. **While shepherds watched their flocks by
   night,**
   All seated on the ground,
   The angel of the Lord came down,
   And glory shone around:

2. 'Fear not!' said he (for mighty dread
   Had seized their troubled mind)
   'Glad tidings of great joy I bring
   To you and all mankind.

3. 'To you in David's town, this day
   Is born, of David's line,
   A Saviour, who is Christ the Lord;
   And this shall be the sign:

4. 'The heavenly babe you there shall find
   To human view displayed.
   All meanly wrapped in swaddling bands,
   And in a manger laid.'

5. Thus spake the angel; and forthwith
   Appeared a shining throng
   Of angels, praising God, who thus
   Addressed their joyful song:

6. 'All glory be to God on high,
   And to the earth be peace;
   Goodwill henceforth from heaven to men
   Begin and never cease.'

286

Betty Lou Mills & Russell J. Mills
© 1968 Chappell Music Ltd.
& International Music Publications

1. **Who took fish and bread, hungry people fed?**
   Who changed water into wine?
   Who made well the sick, who made see the
     blind?
   Who touched earth with feet divine?
   Only Jesus, only Jesus, only He has done
     this:
   Who made live the dead? Truth and
     kindness spread?
   Only Jesus did all this.

2. Who walked dusty road? Cared for young
     and old?
   Who sat children on His knee?
   Who spoke words so wise? Filled men with
     suprise?
   Who gave all, but charged no fee?
   Only Jesus, only Jesus, only He has done
     this:
   Who in death and grief spoke peace to a
     thief?
   Only Jesus did all this.

3. Who soared through the air? Joined His
     Father there?
   He has you and me in view:
   He, who this has done, is God's only Son,
   And He's int'rested in you.
   Only Jesus, only Jesus, only He has done
     this:
   He can change a heart, give a fresh new
     start,
   Only He can do all this.

287

Frances Ridley Havergal 1836-1879
Altered © 1986 Horrobin/Leavers

1. **Who is on the Lord's side?**
   Who will serve the King?
   Who will be His helpers
   Other lives to bring?
   Who will leave the world's side?
   Who will face the foe?
   Who is on the Lord's side?
   Who for Him will go?

   *By His call of mercy,
   Now our lives we bring,
   We are on the Lord's side;
   Jesus, He's our King.*

2. Fierce may be the conflict,
   Strong may be the foe;
   But the King's own army
   None can overthrow.
   Round His standard ranging,
   Victory is secure;
   For His truth unchanging
   Makes the triumph sure.

Joyfully enlisting,
Now our lives we bring,
We are on the Lord's side;
Jesus, He's our King.

3. Chosen to be soldiers
In an alien land,
Chosen, called, and faithful,
For our Captain's band,
In the service royal
Let us not grow cold;
Let us be right loyal,
Noble, true and bold.

Master You will keep us,
Serving You we sing:
Always on the Lord's side,
Jesus, always King.

288 © J.A.P. Booth

1. **Who put the colours in the rainbow?**
Who put the salt into the sea?
Who put the cold into the snowflake?
Who made you and me?
Who put the hump upon the camel?
Who put the neck on the giraffe?
Who put the tail upon the monkey?
Who made hyenas laugh?
Who made whales and snails and quails?
Who made hogs and dogs and frogs?
Who made bats and rats and cats?
Who made ev'rything?

2. Who put the gold into the sunshine?
Who put the sparkle in the stars?
Who put the silver in the moonlight?
Who made Earth and Mars?
Who put the scent into the roses?
Who taught the honey bee to dance?
Who put the tree inside the acorn?
It surely can't be chance!
Who made seas and leaves and trees?
Who made snow and winds that blow?
Who made streams and rivers flow?
God made all of these!

289 © Annie Bush

Who's the king of the jungle?
Who's the king of the sea?
Who's the king of the universe and who's
the king of me?
I'll tell you J-E-S-U-S is,
He's the king of me,
He's the king of the universe, the jungle
and the sea.

290 Priscilla Jane Owens 1829-1899

1. **Will your anchor hold in the storms of life,**
When the clouds unfold their wings of strife?
When the strong tides lift, and the cables
strain,
Will your anchor drift, or firm remain?

We have an anchor that keeps the soul
Steadfast and sure while the billows roll;
Fastened to the rock which cannot move,
Grounded firm and deep in the Saviour's
love!

2. Will your anchor hold in the straits of fear?
When the breakers roar and the reef is near;
While the waters rage, and the wild winds
blow,
Shall the angry waves then your life
o'erflow?
We have an anchor . . .

3. Will your anchor hold in the floods of death,
When the waters cold chill your final
breath?
On the rising tide you can never fail,
While your anchor holds within the veil.
We have an anchor . . .

4. Will your eyes behold through the morning
light
The city of gold and the harbour bright?
Will you anchor safe by the heavenly shore,
When life's storms are past for evermore?
We have an anchor . . .

291 Copyright control

With Jesus in the boat we can smile at the
storm,
Smile at the storm, smile at the storm.
With Jesus in the boat we can smile at the
storm
As we go sailing home.
Sailing, sailing home,
Sailing, sailing home,
With Jesus in the boat we can smile at the
storm
As we go sailing home.

292 C. Austin Miles

Wide, wide as the ocean, high as the
heaven above;
Deep, deep as the deepest sea is my
Saviour's love.
I, though so unworthy, still am a child of His
care;
For His Word teaches me that His love
reaches me everywhere.

293 John Hampden Gurney 1802-1862

1. **Yes, God is good—in earth and sky,**
From ocean depths and spreading wood,
Ten thousand voices seem to cry:
God made us all, and God is good.

2. The sun that keeps His trackless way,
And downward pours His golden flood,
Night's sparkling hosts, all seem to say
In accents clear, that God is good.

3. The joyful birds prolong the strain,
Their song with every spring renewed;
The air we breathe, and falling rain,
Each softly whispers: God is good.

4. I hear it in the rushing breeze;
The hills that have for ages stood,
The echoing sky and roaring seas,
All swell the chorus: God is good.

5. Yes, God is good, all nature says,
By God's own hand with speech endued;
And man, in louder notes of praise,
Should sing for joy that God is good.

6. For all Your gifts we bless You Lord,
But chiefly for our heavenly food;
Your pardoning grace, Your quickening
    word,
These prompt our song, that God is good.

294 Copyright control

**Yesterday, today, for ever, Jesus is the
    same;**
All may change, but Jesus never, Glory to
    His Name!
Glory to His Name! Glory to His Name!
All may change, but Jesus never, Glory to
    His Name!

295 Georgian Banov
© 1978 Sparrow Song/Candle Co
BMG Music Publishing USA

1. **Your ways are higher than mine.**
Your ways are higher than mine.
Your ways are higher than mine.
Much higher.
Your ways are higher than mine.
Your ways are higher than mine.
Your ways are higher than mine.
Much higher.
Higher, higher, much, much, higher,
Higher, higher, much higher.
Higher, higher, much, much, higher,
Higher, higher, much higher.

2. Your thoughts are wiser than mine.
Your thoughts are wiser than mine.
Your thoughts are wiser than mine.
Much wiser.
Your thoughts are wiser than mine.
Your thoughts are wiser than mine.
Your thoughts are wiser than mine.
Much wiser.
Wiser, wiser, much, much, wiser,
Wiser, wiser, much wiser.
Wiser, wiser, much, much, wiser,
Wiser, wiser, much wiser.

3. Your strength is greater than mine.
Your strength is greater than mine.
Your strength is greater than mine.
Much greater.
Your strength is greater than mine.
Your strength is greater than mine.
Your strength is greater than mine.
Much greater.
Greater, greater, much, much, greater,
Greater, greater, much greater.
Greater, greater, much, much, greater,
Greater, greater, much greater.

Hallelujah, Hallelujah,
Hallelujah, Hallelu.
Hallelujah, Hallelujah,
Hallelujah, Hallelu.

296 M. Ford
© 1978 Springtide/Word Music (UK)

You are the King of Glory,
You are the Prince of Peace,
You are the Lord of heav'n and earth,
You're the Son of righteousness.
Angels bow down before You,
Worship and adore, for
You have the words of eternal life,
You are Jesus Christ the Lord.
Hosanna to the Son of David!
Hosanna to the King of kings!
Glory in the highest heaven,
For Jesus the Messiah reigns.

297 J. Cowans
© 1970 Salvationist Publishing & Supplies

1. **You can't stop rain from falling down,**
Prevent the sun from shining,
You can't stop spring from coming in,
Or winter from resigning,
Or still the waves or stay the winds,
Or keep the day from dawning;
You can't stop God from loving you,
His love is new each morning.

2. You can't stop ice from being cold,
You can't stop fire from burning,
Or hold the tide that's going out,
Delay its sure returning,

Or halt the progress of the years,
The flight of fame and fashion;
You can't stop God from loving you,
His nature is compassion.

3. You can't stop God from loving you,
   Though you may disobey Him,
   You can't stop God from loving you,
   However you betray Him;
   From love like this no pow'r on earth
   The human heart can sever,
   You can't stop God from loving you,
   Not God, not now, nor ever.

298

E.H. Plumptre 1821-1891

1. **Your hand, O God has guided**
   Your flock, from age to age;
   Your faithfulness is written
   On history's open page.
   Our fathers knew Your goodness,
   And we their deeds record;
   And both to this bear witness:
   One church, one faith, One Lord.

2. Your heralds brought the gospel
   To greatest as to least;
   They summoned men to hasten
   And share the great king's feast.
   And this was all their teaching
   In every deed and word;
   To all alike proclaiming:
   One church, one faith, One Lord.

3. Through many days of darkness,
   Through many scenes of strife,
   The faithful few fought bravely
   To guard the nation's life.
   Their gospel of redemption—
   Sin pardoned, man restored;
   Was all in this enfolded:
   One church, one faith, One Lord.

4. Your mercy will not fail us
   Nor leave Your work undone;
   With Your right hand to help us,
   The victory shall be won.
   And then by earth and heaven
   Your name shall be adored;
   And this shall be their anthem:
   One church, one faith, One Lord.

299
after E.L. Budry 1854-1932
R.B. Hoyle 1875-1939
© World Student Christian Federation,
in this version Jubilate Hymns

1. **Yours be the glory! risen, conquering Son;**
   Endless is the victory over death You won;
   Angels robed in splendour rolled the stone
   away,
   Kept the folded grave clothes where Your
   body lay:

Yours be the glory! risen, conquering Son:
Endless is the victory over death You won.

2. See! Jesus meets us, risen from the tomb,
   Lovingly he greets us, scatters fear and
   gloom;
   Let the church with gladness hymns of
   triumph sing!
   For her Lord is living, death has lost its
   sting
   Yours be the glory . . .

3. No more we doubt you, glorious prince of
   life:
   What is life without you? aid us in our strife;
   Make us more than conquerors, through
   your deathless love,
   Bring us safe through Jordan to your home
   above:
   Yours be the glory . . .

300
Copyright control

Zaccheus was a very little man,
And a very little man was he.
He climbed up into a sycamore tree,
For the Saviour he wanted to see.
And when the Saviour passed that way,
He looked into the tree and said,
'Now, Zaccheus, you come down,
For I'm coming to your house to tea.'

301
© 1986 Peter Horrobin

1. **Lord we ask now to receive Your blessing,**
   Lord we ask now to receive Your love.
   Come, we pray; Come, we pray
   And lead us hour by hour.
   Bless, we ask, our friends and close
   relations
   Let them feel Your touch of loving power.

2. Lord we trust You to give us Your blessing,
   Lord we trust You to give us Your love
   As we give; As we give
   Our lives afresh to You.
   Take, we ask, all that we have and are,
   Lord,
   Let them now be used in service true.

3. Lord we give to others now Your blessing,
   Lord we give to others now Your love.
   As we share; As we share
   With them the life You've giv'n.
   Yes we will in harmony with You, Lord,
   Let them see in us a touch of heav'n.

302
Paul Field
© 1991 Daybreak Music Ltd

1. **A naggy mum, a grumpy dad, a brother
   who's a pain.**
   A sister who takes toys and never gives them
   back again.

   *All the same, all the same,
   in sunshine and in rain.
   No matter who we are you know
   God loves us all the same.*

2. An auntie who cooks sprouts for tea and
   makes you eat them all.
   A grandad who tells terrible jokes and drives
   you up the wall.
   All the same . . .

3. An uncle who forgets about your birthday
   when it comes.
   A teacher who gets cross with you and makes
   you do more sums.
   All the same . . .

303
From John 13
© in this version Jubilate Hymns

A new commandment that I give to you,
is to love one another as I have loved you,
is to love one another as I have loved you.

By this shall all men know you are My
   disciples,
if you have love one for another;
by this shall all men know you are My
   disciples,
if you have love one for another.

304
© Timothy Dudley-Smith

1. **A purple robe, a crown of thorn,**
   a reed in His right hand;
   before the soldiers' spite and scorn
   I see my Saviour stand.

2. He bears between the Roman guard
   the weight of all our woe;
   a stumbling figure bowed and scarred
   I see my Saviour go.

3. Fast to the cross's spreading span,
   high in the sunlit air,
   all the unnumbered sins of man
   I see my Saviour bear.

4. He hangs, by whom the world was made,
   beneath the darkened sky;
   the everlasting ransom paid,
   I see my Saviour die.

5. He shares on high His Father's throne,
   who once in mercy came;
   for all His love to sinners shown
   I sing my Saviour's name.

305
© 1992 Laura and Heather Bradley

1. **A special star is in the sky**
   to lead the way (to lead the way);
   a tiny stable cold and lonely
   where they can stay (where they can stay).

   *But our hearts have been warm,
   since the day Jesus Christ was born,
   and that's the way it shall stay,
   because He is the Way, the Truth and the
      Life, (the Truth and the Life).*

2. The shepherds left their flocks behind
   to see the Babe (to see the Babe);
   the angel told them to bring a gift so
   a lamb they gave (a lamb they gave).
   But our hearts . . .

3. The wise men came from lands afar,
   on camels they rode, (on camels they rode);
   the gifts they offered were frankincense,
   myrrh and gold (myrrh and gold).
   But our hearts . . .

306
Paul Field
© 1991 Daybreak Music Ltd

1. **A wiggly waggly worm, a slippery slimy
      slug,**
   a creepy crawly buzzy thing, a tickly wickly
      bug.
   Of all the things to be, I'm happy that I'm me.
   Thank You Lord, I'm happy that I'm me.

   I'm happy that I'm me, happy that I'm me.
   There's no one else in all the world that I
      would rather be.
   A wiggly waggly worm, a slippery slimy slug,
   a creepy crawly buzzy thing, a tickly wickly
      bug.

2. A prickly porcupine, a clumsy kangaroo,
   a croaky frog, a hairy hog, a monkey in a zoo.
   Of all the things to be, I'm happy that I'm me.
   Thank You Lord, I'm happy that I'm me.

   I'm happy that I'm me, happy that I'm me.
   There's no-one else in all the world that I
      would rather be.
   A prickly porcupine, a clumsy kangaroo,
   a croaky frog, a hairy dog, a monkey in a zoo.

307 Paul Field and Ralph Chambers
© 1991 Daybreak Music Ltd

All you have to do is to ask the Lord
to forgive the wrong things you have done.
Tell Him that you're sorry you have hurt Him,
and then believe that Jesus is God's Son.
He died on the cross to be your Saviour,
rose from the dead to be your special friend.
Ask Him in your heart, make a brand new
   start.
Love and serve Him till your life shall end.

308 Copyright control

1. **Alleluia.** *(8 times)*

2. How I love Him.

3. Blessed Jesus.

4. My Redeemer.

5. Jesus, Master.

6. Alleluia.

309 © 1983 Kathie Hill and Jane McMahan
1986 by John T. Benson Co./United Nations Music
Publishing/Boosey & Hawkes Music Publishers Ltd

Are you humbly grateful
or grumbly hateful?
What's your attitude?
Do you grumble and groan,
or let it be known
you're grateful for all
God's done for you?

1. When Jonah found himself
  in the belly of a whale,
  did he cause a riot inside?
  No!
  He headed for shore—
  with his message from God
  and thanked the Lord
  for his free ride.
  Phew!
    Are you humbly grateful . . .

2. When Noah found himself
  in the floating zoo,
  did he ever try to jump ship?
  No!
  For forty long days
  and for forty long nights
  he cleared the deck
  on that long trip!
  Phew!
    Are you humbly grateful . . .

       Which one are you?
(Spoken) Which one are you?

310 Peter and Hanneke Jacobs
© 1988 Maranatha Music/Word Music (UK)

And we know that all things,
all things, all things work together for good;
yes we know that all things,
all things, all things work together for good!
To them that love the Lord,
to them that love the Lord,
to them that love the Lord,
and are called according to His purpose.
And we know that all things,
all things, all things work together for good;
yes we know that all things,
all things, all things work together for good.
Romans eight, verse twenty eight.

311 © 1980 S Lesley Scott

1. **At harvest time we celebrate**
  God's gift to us of food and drink.
  We thank Him for the care He's shown
  for farmers and the seeds they've sown.

  Praise the Lord! Praise the Lord!
  Praise the Lord! Praise the Lord!
  Praise the Lord! Praise the Lord!
  Thank Him for harvest.

2. God's watched the fields through day and
    night,
  He's given the seeds both dark and light.
  He's watered them with fresh cool rain
  and now there's fields and fields of grain.
    Praise the Lord . . .

3. God helps the farmers cut the corn,
  He keeps the weather dry and warm,
  until it's baled and brought inside,
  before the start of wintertide.
    Praise the Lord . . .

4. Now once the crops are in their barns
  there's work to do still on the farms.
  It's time to put the crops to use
  to make the different kinds of foods.
    Praise the Lord . . .

5. At harvest time we celebrate
  God's gifts to us of food and drink.
  Let's sing and clap to show our thanks
  for all the care God takes of us.
    Praise the Lord . . .
    Praise the Lord . . .

312 Anon
Copyright control

Be careful little hands what you do,
be careful little hands what you do.
There's a Father up above who is looking
    down in love,
so be careful little hands what you do.

313

Geoffrey Ainger
© 1964, 1972 Stainer & Bell Ltd

1. **Born in the night,**
   Mary's child,
   a long way from Your home:
   coming in need,
   Mary's child,
   born in a borrowed room.

2. Clear shining light,
   Mary's child,
   Your face lights up our way:
   Light of the World,
   Mary's child,
   dawn on our darkened day.

3. Truth of our life,
   Mary's child,
   You tell us God is good:
   prove it is true,
   Mary's child,
   go to Your cross of wood.

4. Hope of the world,
   Mary's child,
   You're coming soon to reign:
   King of the earth,
   Mary's child,
   walk in our streets again.

314

© 1991 Allan Brown

1. **Be holy in all that you do,**
   be holy in all that you do;
   be holy in all that you do today,
   be holy in all that you do.
   You are a chosen people,
   be holy in all that you do;
   you are a chosen people,
   be holy in all that you do.

2. Be holy in all that you say . . .

3. Be holy in all that you think . . .

4. Be holy in all that you are . . .

315

Valerie Ruddle and William Horton
© Oxford University Press from
New Songs of Praise 5

*Bring your Christingle with gladness and
   joy!*
*Sing praise to God who gave us His Son;
so give Him, give Him your love.*

LEADER
1. Here is an orange—
   ALL
   An orange as round as the world that God
      made.
   Bring your Christingle . . .

LEADER
2. Here is a candle—
   ALL
   A candle for Jesus, the Light of the world,
   an orange as round as the world that God
      made;
      Bring your Christingle . . .

LEADER
3. Here is red ribbon—
   ALL
   Red ribbon reminds us Christ died for us all;
   a candle for Jesus, the Light of the world;
   an orange as round as the world that God
      made;
      Bring your Christingle . . .

LEADER
4. Here are the fruits—
   ALL
   The fruits of the earth God has given us to
      share;
   red ribbon reminds us Christ died for us all;
   a candle for Jesus, the Light of the world;
   an orange as round as the world that God
      made;
      Bring your Christingle . . .

316

© Geoffrey Marshall-Taylor/Jubilate Hymns

1. **Can you be sure that the rain will fall?**
   Can you be sure that birds will fly?
   Can you be sure that rivers will flow,
   or that the sun will light the sky?

   *God has promised.
   God never breaks a promise He makes.
   His Word is always true.*

2. Can you be sure that the tide will turn?
   Can you be sure that grass will grow?
   Can you be sure that night will come,
   or that the sun will melt the snow?
      God has promised . . .

3. You can be sure that God is near,
   you can be sure He won't let you down;
   you can be sure He'll always hear;
   and that He's given Jesus, His Son.
      God has promised . . .

317

Paul Field
© 1991 Daybreak Music Ltd

1. **Can you count the stars shining in the sky?**
   Can you hold the moonlight in your hand?
   Can you stop the waves rolling on the shore,
   or find the place where rainbows meet the
      land?

   *I've got a Friend, who knows how all these
      things are done;
   Jesus Lord of all, God's only Son*

2. Up in outer space, planets spinning round,
millions more than we can ever see.
It's hard to understand how God, who made it
   all,
still cares about someone like you and me.
   I've got a Friend . . .

318 Janette Smart
© Lillenas Publishing Co/Thankyou Music

1. **Can you imagine how it feels to know**
the God who made the earth and sky and
   sea?
When He created all the universe,
His mighty plan included you and me.

   Well, this experience is not imagination;
   it's a fact, oh yes, it's true.
   And I just can't keep it to myself;
   I'll pass it on to you.

2. Can you imagine how it feels to have
a Friend who never slumbers, never sleeps?
Can you believe that when He comes into
your heart and says He'll live there, it's for
   keeps?

   Well, this experience is not imagination;
   it's a fact, oh yes, it's true.
   And I just can't keep it to myself;
   I'll pass it on to you,
   and you, and you, and you.

319 © Timothy Dudley-Smith

1. **Christ be my leader by night as by day;**
safe through the darkness,
   for He is the way.
Gladly I follow, my future His care;
darkness is daylight when Jesus is there.

2. Christ be my teacher in age as in youth,
drifting or doubting, for He is the truth.
Grant me to trust Him,
   though shifting as sand,
doubt cannot daunt me, in Jesus I stand.

3. Christ be my Saviour in calm as in strife;
death cannot hold me, for He is the life.
Not darkness nor doubting
   nor sin and its stain
can touch my salvation: with Jesus I reign.

320 Joe E. Parks
© Singspiration/United Nations Music Publishing/
Boose & Hawkes Music Publishers Ltd

1. **Children, join the celebration**
on this happy Easter day;
Christ the Lord is risen as He said!
Mary on that early morning
heard the angel gladly say:
'Jesus lives—He is no longer dead!'

2. Praise Him now with songs of gladness,
sing triumphant hymns of praise:
Christ the Lord is risen as He said!
Children, join the celebration,
with the hosts of heaven say:
'Jesus Christ, our Saviour, lives today!'

321 Ernie and Debbie Rettino
© Rettino/Kerner Publishing/administered by
Maranatha Music/Word Music/UK

Christmas is a time, Christmas is a time,
Christmas is a time to love.
Christmas is a time, Christmas is a time,
Christmas is a time to love.

We often start to worry, and people get upset
if things don't all go right on Christmas day.
What we should remember in all the push and
   shove,
is Christmas is a time of love.

Christmas is a time, Christmas is a time,
Christmas is a time to love.
Christmas is a time, Christmas is a time,
Christmas is a time to love.

322 Jimmy and Carol Owens
© 1980 Communique Music Inc./United Nations
Music Publishing Ltd/Boosey & Hawkes Music
Publishers Ltd

Christmas isn't Christmas till it happens in
   your heart;
somewhere deep inside you is where
   Christmas really starts.
So give your heart to Jesus; you'll discover
   when you do
that it's Christmas, really Christmas for you.

Jesus brings warmth like a winter fire,
a light like a candle's glow.
He's waiting now to come inside
as He did so long ago.
Jesus brings gifts of truth and life,
and makes them bloom and grow.
So welcome Him with a song of joy,
and when He comes, you'll know,

that Christmas isn't Christmas till it happens
   in your heart;
somewhere deep inside you is where
   Christmas really starts.
So give your heart to Jesus; you'll discover
   when you do
that it's Christmas, really Christmas;
Christmas, really Christmas for you.

323 Valeris Collison
© 1972 High-Fye Music Ltd

Come and join the celebration,
it's a very special day;
come and share our jubilation,
there's a new King born today!

1. See the shepherds
   hurry down to Bethlehem;
   gaze in wonder
   at the Son of God who lay before them.
   Come and join . . .

2. Wise men journey,
   led to worship by a star;
   kneel in homage,
   bringing precious gifts from lands afar, so
   Come and join . . .

3. 'God is with us,'
   'round the world the message bring;
   He is with us,
   'Welcome!' all the bells on earth are pealing.
   Come and join . . .

324

From Psalm 95
© 1987 Ruth Hooke

BOYS **Come let us sing for joy to the Lord.**

GIRLS Come let us sing for joy to the Lord.

BOYS We will sing, we will sing, we will sing.

GIRLS We will sing, we will sing, we will sing.

BOYS Let us shout aloud to the Rock of our
salvation.

GIRLS Let us shout aloud to the Rock of our
salvation.

BOYS We will shout! We will shout! We will
shout!

GIRLS We will shout! We will shout! We will
shout!

ALL For the Lord is the great God, the great
King above all gods.

BOYS Splendour and majesty,

GIRLS splendour and majesty,

BOYS are before Him,

GIRLS are before Him.

BOYS Strength and glory,

GIRLS strength and glory,

ALL are in His sanctuary.

325

Patricia Morgan and Dave Bankhead
© 1984 Thankyou Music

Come on and celebrate!
His gift of love we will celebrate—
the Son of God, who loved us
and gave us life.

We'll shout Your praise, O King:
You give us joy nothing else can bring;
we'll give to You our offering
in celebration praise.

Come on and celebrate, celebrate,
celebrate and sing,
celebrate and sing to the King.
Come on and celebrate, celebrate,
celebrate and sing,
celebrate and sing to the King!

326

© Carolyn Keates

Counting, counting, one, two, three,
clap my hands and
sing for joy, for
God made ME!
Three, four, five, six, and number seven too;
shout it aloud, make
sure you're heard, for
God made YOU!

1. I have ten toes, ten fingers,
   two legs on which I stand,
   an arm on either side of me,
   at the end of each a hand;
   a right ear and a left ear,
   a head to shake and nod,
   two eyes, one nose, a mouth, a voice
   to whisper or to SHOUT!
   Counting, counting . . .

2. God made me very different
   from everyone I see,
   my size and shape and colour,
   He chose it carefully.
   God is so very clever
   He made the whole world too;
   He put the life in everything
   including me and you.
   Counting, counting . . .

327

Ian White
© Little Misty Music Ltd

1. **Crackers and turkeys and pudding and**
   cream,
   toys in the windows that I've never seen.
   This is the Christmas that everyone sees,
   but Christmas means more to me.

   It's somebody's birthday I won't forget,
   as I open the things that I get.
   I'll remember the inn and the stable so bare,
   and Jesus who once lay there.

2. Everyone's out shopping late every night,
   for candles and presents and Christmas tree
      lights.
   This is the Christmas that everyone sees,
   but Christmas means more to me.
   It's somebody's birthday . . .

3. Christmas morning, the start of the day,
   there's presents to open and new games to
   play.
   This is the Christmas that everyone sees,
   but Christmas means more to me.
   It's somebody's birthday . . .

328
Ralph Chambers
© 1991 Daybreak Music Ltd

Don't know much about the ozone layer,
Rain forests seem miles away.
But each of us can be a player,
fight to save the world God has made.
This is God's world.
This is God's world,
and you're a member of the human race.
This is God's world.
This is God's world.
This is God's world.
Let's try to make it a better place.

329
Frances Towle Rath
© 1974 Child Evangelism Fellowship Inc

1. **Did you ever talk to God above?**
   Tell Him that you need a friend to love.
   Pray in Jesus' name believing
   that God answers prayer.

2. Have you told Him all your cares and woes?
   Every tiny little fear He knows.
   You can know He'll always hear
   and He will answer prayer.

3. You can whisper in a crowd to Him.
   You can cry when you're alone to Him.
   You don't have to pray out loud to Him;
   He knows your thoughts.

4. On a lofty mountain peak, He's there.
   In a meadow by a stream, He's there.
   Anywhere on earth you go
   He's been there from the start.

5. Find the answers in His Word; it's true.
   You'll be strong because He walks with you.
   By His faithfulness He'll change you too.
   God answers prayer.

330
Sam Horner
© 1991 Daybreak Music Ltd

1. **Even if I don't like the way things went
   today.**
   Even if I'm feeling down, I'll praise You
   anyway.
   If I'm feeling lonely, if I'm feeling bad,
   I'll think about the things You've done, and
   even when I'm sad:

I will worship You in spirit and in truth,
I will worship You in spirit and in truth,
I will worship You in spirit and in truth,
I will worship You in spirit and in truth.

2. When my life is going great, when everything
   is right,
   help me not to forget You, Lord, or keep You
   out of sight.
   I don't want to leave You out, not even for a
   day;
   I want to see Your hand at work and hear the
   words You say.
   I will worship You . . .

331
© 1992 Greg Leavers

1. **Every day if you go astray**
   stop! and turn around.
   Then don't worry if you've said sorry
   stop! and turn around.
   When we come to Jesus
   He says He'll forgive us,
   for He cares about us.
   This is what He promises.
   When we come to Jesus
   He says He'll forgive us
   for He cares about us all.

2. Every day as we walk God's way
   stop! and praise the Lord.
   He will change us for He's living in us:
   stop! and praise the Lord.
   Jesus You forgive us,
   then bring Your life to us
   through Your Holy Spirit.
   This is what You promise us.
   Jesus You forgive us,
   then bring Your life to us
   through Your Spirit in our lives.

3. Jesus, Saviour, Redeemer and King,
   let's go! and live for Him.
   Son of God our helper and friend,
   go! and live for Him.
   Jesus how we thank You,
   Jesus how we love You,
   Jesus help us trust You
   till the day You come again.
   Jesus how we thank You,
   Jesus how we love You,
   Jesus help us trust You more.

332
© 1992 Greg Leavers

Everybody join in singing this song,
thanking God for all the good things He's
done;
showing love for us through Jesus His Son,

good and bad and the weak and strong.
Young and old all can sing along:
come on everybody sing this song.

1. Thank God for the gift of life.
   Thank Him for His care.
   When our lives then get messed up,
   He'll clear out the bad things there.
       Everybody join in singing . . .

2. In our lives God wants to live,
   make His presence known.
   If we're sorry He'll forgive,
   then our hearts can be His home.
       Everybody join in singing . . .

333   Derek and Jackie Llewellyn
          © 1990 Sea Dream Music

Everyone in the whole wide world
matters to our friend Jesus.
Everyone, every boy or girl,
we all matter to Him.

1. Jump up if you're wearing red.
                          (Jump up)
   Wave your arms if you're wearing blue.
                          (Wave)
   Clap your hands if you're wearing green.
                          (Clap)
   Stamp your feet if you're wearing shoes.
                          (Stamp)
       Everyone in the whole wide world . . .

2. Jump up if you've ridden a bike.
                          (Jump)
   Wave your arms if you've flown in a plane.
                          (Wave)
   Clap your hands if you've been in a car.
                          (Clap)
   Stamp your feet if you've been on a train.
                          (Stamp)
       Everyone in the whole wide world . . .

334   Ian White
          © Little Misty Music Ltd

Everywhere He walks with me,
and through prayer He talks with me.
He has cared enough for me,
to die to set me free.

1. Since then you have been raised with Christ,
   set your heart on things above.
   Where Christ is seated at God's right hand,
   set your minds on things above.
       Everywhere He walks with me . . .

2. Put to death whatever is sin,
   rid yourselves of all these things.
   You have been renewed in the Lord,
   and He is all, and is in all.
       Everywhere He walks with me . . .

3. Let His peace now rule in your hearts.
   Let His Word be rich in you.
   Sing psalms and hymns with thanks to God,
   praise Him in all that you do.
       Everywhere He walks with me . . .

335   © 1990 Greg Leavers

1. **Father be with *her/his/their family,**
   as they cry with sadness today.
   Aching hearts feeling such a loss:
   may they know Your love.

2. Comfort them with Your love, oh Lord,
   as they try to understand
   why You called *her/him/them to be with You:
   may they know Your peace.

* (Use the relevant word or use the child's name)

336   © 1990 Greg Leavers

1. **Father, for our friends we pray,**
   please be near to them today;
   in their sadness, through their tears,
   may they know Your peace.

2. Now that he/she is by Your side
   comfort friends when they ask 'why'.
   Their dear loved one had to die;
   may they know Your love.

3. Though part of their lives has gone,
   give them strength to carry on.
   As they face the days to come,
   may they know Your care.

337   Ian Smale
          © 1984 Glorie Music/Thankyou Music

Father God, I wonder
how I managed to exist
without the knowledge
of Your parenthood
and Your loving care.
But now I am Your son,
I am adopted in Your family,
and I can never be alone
'cause, Father God,
You're there beside me.

I will sing Your praises,
I will sing Your praises,
I will sing Your praises for evermore.
I will sing Your praises,
I will sing Your praises,
I will sing Your praises for evermore.

338

Paul Crouch
© Daybreak Music Ltd

Father, Your Word is like a light in the darkness.
Father, Your Word is like a sharp, sharp sword.
Father, Your Word is like a stream in the desert.
There's nothing that compares with the wisdom of Your Word.

339 (i)

From Psalm 147
© Timothy Dudley-Smith

1. **Fill your hearts with joy and gladness,**
sing and praise your God and mine!
Great the Lord in love and wisdom,
might and majesty divine!
He who framed the starry heavens
knows and names them as they shine.

2. Praise the Lord, His people, praise Him!
wounded souls His comfort know;
those who fear Him find His mercies,
peace for pain and joy for woe;
humble hearts are high exalted,
human pride and power laid low.

3. Praise the Lord for times and seasons,
cloud and sunshine, wind and rain;
spring to melt the snows of winter
till the waters flow again;
grass upon the mountain pastures,
golden valleys thick with grain.

4. Fill your hearts with joy and gladness,
peace and plenty crown your days;
love His laws, declare His judgements,
walk in all His words and ways;
He the Lord and we His children—
praise the Lord, all people, praise!

339 (ii)

From Psalm 147
© Timothy Dudley-Smith

1. **Fill your hearts with joy and gladness,**
sing and praise your God and mine!
Great the Lord in love and wisdom,
might and majesty divine!
He who framed the starry heavens
knows and names them as they shine,
knows and names them as they shine.

2. Praise the Lord, His people, praise Him!
wounded souls His comfort know;
those who fear Him find His mercies,
peace for pain and joy for woe;
humble hearts are high exalted,
human pride and power laid low,
human pride and power laid low.

3. Praise the Lord for times and seasons,
cloud and sunshine, wind and rain;
spring to melt the snows of winter
till the waters flow again;
grass upon the mountain pastures,
golden valleys thick with grain,
golden valleys thick with grain.

4. Fill your hearts with joy and gladness,
peace and plenty crown your days;
love His laws, declare His judgements,
walk in all His words and ways;
He the Lord and we His children—
praise the Lord, all people, praise!
praise the Lord, all people, praise!

340

Paul Crouch
© 1992 Daybreak Music Ltd

For the foolishness of God is wiser than man's wisdom,
and the weakness of God is stronger than man's strength.
For the foolishness of God is wiser than man's wisdom,
and the weakness of God is stronger than man's strength.
For the foolishness of God is wiser than man's wisdom,
and the weakness of God is stronger than man's strength.
For the foolishness of God is wiser than man's wisdom,
and the weakness of God is stronger than man's strength.

God knows all about the world, the things we cannot see,
the things that we don't understand that baffle you and me.
His strength is never ending and we are weak and small.
His hand supports the universe and He is in control.

For the foolishness of God . . .

341

Graham Kendrick
© 1983 Thankyou Music

1. **From heaven You came, helpless babe,**
entered our world, Your glory veiled,
not to be served but to serve,
and give Your life that we might live.

   This is our God, the Servant King,
   He calls us now to follow Him,
   to bring our lives as a daily offering
   of worship to the Servant King.

2. There in the garden of tears
my heavy load He chose to bear;
His heart with sorrow was torn,
'Yet not my will but yours,' He said.
   This is our God . . .

3. Come see His hands and His feet,
   the scars that speak of sacrifice,
   hands that flung stars into space
   to cruel nails surrendered.
   This is our God . . .

4. So let us learn how to serve
   and in our lives enthrone Him,
   each other's needs to prefer,
   for it is Christ we're serving.
   This is our God . . .

342 © 1990 Greg Leavers

From my knees to my nose,
from my head to my toes,
does God know all about me?
If I'm happy or sad,
if I'm good or I'm bad,
does God know all about me?
The answer is yes
and He loves me the best,
though He knows everything about me.
The answer is yes
and He loves me the best,
and He knows that my name is . . . *(shout
name)*

343 C. Powell and K. Wood
© 1991 Sea Dream Music

Get up out of bed,
have a yawn and scratch your head
and say, 'Thank You, it's a brand new day.'

Stretch out, touch your toes,
blink your eyes and blow your nose
and say, 'Thank You, it's a brand new day.'

1. Jesus taught us all to go His way.
   Get out of bed and go with Him today.
   Get up out of bed . . .

2. Jesus showed us that He can make us new.
   Get out of bed and ask Him what to do.
   Get up out of bed . . .

3. Jesus loves us all just like He said.
   Get out of bed and shake your sleepy head.
   Get up out of bed . . .

344 M. Sargent (1895–1967)
© Oxford University Press, and in this version
Word and Music/Jubilate Hymns

1. **Girls and boys, leave your toys, make no
   noise,**
   kneel at His crib and worship Him.
   For this shrine, Child divine, is the sign
   our Saviour's here.
   Alleluia, the church bells ring.

'Alleluia!' the angels sing,
alleluia from everything—
all must draw near!

2. On that day, far away, Jesus lay—
   angels were watching round His head.
   Holy Child, mother mild, undefiled,
   we sing Your praise.
   Alleluia . . .
   our hearts we raise.

3. Shepherds came at the fame of Your name,
   angels their guide to Bethlehem;
   in that place, saw Your face filled with grace,
   stood at Your door.
   Alleluia . . .
   love evermore.

345 Janet Morgan
© 1989 Sea Dream Music

Give thanks to the Lord for He is good.
Give thanks to the Lord forever.
Give thanks to the Lord for He is good.

1. When you jump out of bed
   and you touch your toes,
   when you brush your teeth
   and put on your clothes,
   Give thanks . . .

2. When you eat your dinner
   and you're all full up,
   when your Mum says (Name)
   and you help wash up,
   Give thanks . . .

3. When you stretch up high
   and you touch the ground,
   when you stretch out wide
   and you turn around,
   Give thanks . . .

4 When you click your fingers
   and you stamp your feet,
   when you clap your hands
   and you slap your knees,
   Give thanks . . .
   Give thanks to the Lord. Amen.

346 © 1992 Gillian E. Hutchinson

1. **God has made me, and He knows me,**
   He will listen to my prayer.
   Understanding, ever loving,
   He's the God who's always there.
   Even though He made the world,
   He knows my name and cares for me.
   He will hear me when I call Him;
   in His heart I'll always be.

2. Help me, Lord to understand
   that I'm a child who's loved by You.
   You'll protect me, and be with me
   in the things I have to do.
   Thank You Lord, that I can trust You,
   thank You for the love You bring.
   Thank You that You'll never leave me;
   Father God, Your praise I sing.

347
Fred Pratt Green
© 1979 Stainer & Bell Ltd

1. **God in His love for us lent us this planet,**
   gave it a purpose in time and in space:
   small as a spark from the fire of creation,
   cradle of life and the home of our race.

2. Thanks be to God for its bounty and beauty,
   life that sustains us in body and mind:
   plenty for all, if we learn how to share it,
   riches undreamed of to fathom and find.

3. Long have the wars of man ruined its harvest;
   long has earth bowed to the terror of force;
   long have we wasted what others have need
      of,
   poisoned the fountain of life at its source.

4. Earth is the Lord's: it is ours to enjoy it;
   ours, as His stewards, to farm and defend.
   From its pollution, misuse and destruction,
   good Lord deliver us, world without end!

348
Anon
Copyright control

God loves you, and I love you,
and that's the way it should be.
God loves you, and I love you,
and that's the way it should be.

1. You can be happy, and I can be happy,
   and that's the way it should be.
   You can be happy, and I can be happy,
   and that's the way it should be.
      God loves you . . .

2. You can be very sad, I can be very sad;
   and that's the way it can be.
   You can be very sad, I can be very sad;
   and that's the way it can be.
      God loves you . . .

3. We can love others like sisters and brothers,
   and that's the way it should be.
   We can love others like sisters and brothers,
   and that's the way it should be.
      God loves you . . .

349
Derek Llewellyn
© 1990 Sea Dream Music

1. **God loves you so much,**
   God wants you so much,
   God wants to tell you so much
   that He put it in a book for you.

   And it's the Bible,
   yes it's the Bible,
   oh it's the Bible.
   Yes He put it in a letter
   so we could know Him better.

2. He wants to know you so much,
   He wants to show you so much,
   God wants to tell you so much
   that He put it in a book for you.
      And it's the Bible . . .

3. God loves you so much,
   God wants you so much,
   God wants to tell you so much
   that He put it in a book,
   put in a book for,
   put in a book for you.

350
© 1990 Fiona Inkpen

1. **God of all mercy,**
   Your forgiveness and compassion
2. call forth songs from within
   that fill our hearts with gladness.

351
© 1990 Greg Leavers

God told Joshua to take Jericho.
God told Joshua to take Jericho.
He said, 'Do it My way',
Joshua said, 'OK'.
So through faith the city walls came down!

1. Marching round the city,
   priests are at the front,
   blowing on their trumpets,
   going round just once.
   This they did for six days,
   just as God had said;
   the Priests were making all the noise the rest
      were saying,
      God told Joshua . . .

2. God said on day seven,
   'Here is what you do:
   march around for six times,
   then do something new.
   When you're on lap seven,
   Jericho look out!
   All their walls will crumble when you give a
   great big SHOUT!!'
     God told Joshua . . .

352 © Peter Lewis

1. **God was there before the world was made.**
   God is here, He's with us every day.
   God is love and that will never change.
   Yesterday, today, forever
   He's the same.
   Yesterday, today, forever
   He's the same.

2. God is good, the Bible tells us so.
   God is wise, He knows what we don't know.
   God is true, no matter what we do.
   Yesterday, today, forever
   our life through.
   Yesterday, today, forever
   our life through.

3. God is like a Father to us all.
   God will always listen when we call.
   God's the one we worship and adore.
   Yesterday, today, forever
   He is Lord.
   Yesterday, today, forever
   He is Lord.

353 © Timothy Dudley-Smith

1. **God whose love is everywhere**
   made our earth and all things fair,
   ever keeps them in His care;
     praise the God of love!
   He who hung the stars in space
   holds the spinning world in place;
     praise the God of love!

2. Come with thankful songs to sing
   of the gifts the seasons bring,
   summer, winter, autumn, spring;
     praise the God of love!
   He who gave us breath and birth
   gives us all the fruitful earth;
     praise the God of love!

3. Mark what love the Lord displayed,
   all our sins upon Him laid,
   by His blood our ransom paid;
     praise the God of love!
   Circled by that scarlet band

all the world is in His hand;
  praise the God of love!

4 See the sign of love appear,
  flame of glory, bright and clear,
  light for all the world is here;
    praise the God of love!
  Gloom and darkness, get you gone!
  Christ the Light of life has shone;
    praise the God of love!

354 Ian White
© Little Misty Music Ltd

Going up to Jerusalem,
going up to Jerusalem,
going up to Jerusalem, (Jesus going up),
going up to Jerusalem, (Jesus going up).
Going up to Jerusalem,
going up to Jerusalem,
going up to Jerusalem, (Jesus going up),
going up to Jerusalem.

1. Hosanna, hosanna,
   we lay our branches down.
   Hosanna, hosanna,
   the King is coming to our town.
   Hosanna, hosanna today.

2. He's the Saviour, He's the Saviour
   we lay our branches down.
   He's the Saviour. He's the Saviour
   the King is coming to our town.
   Hosanna, hosanna today.

355 Paul Crouch and David Mudie
© 1989 Daybreak Music Ltd

1. **Grace is when God gives us**
   the things we don't deserve.
   Grace is when God gives us
   the things we don't deserve.
   He does it because He loves us.
   He does it because He loves us.
   Grace is when God gives us
   the things we don't deserve.

2. Mercy is when God gives us
   the things we don't deserve.
   Mercy is when God gives us
   the things we don't deserve.
   He does it because He loves us.
   He does it because He loves us.
   Mercy is when God gives us
   the things we don't deserve.

356

Richard Hubbard
© 1989 Thankyou Music

1. **Hang on, stand still,**
   stay put, hold tight;
   wait for the Spirit of God.
   Don't push, don't shove,
   don't move, that's right;
   just wait for the Spirit of God.
   Hang on . . .

   For you will receive the power of God.
   You will receive the power of God.
   You will receive the power of God
   when the Holy Spirit is upon you.

2. Let go, launch out,
   press on, don't fight;
   be filled with the Spirit of God.
   Move on, make way,
   step out, that's right;
   be filled with the Spirit of God.
   Let go . . .

   For you have received the power of God.
   You have received the power of God.
   You have received the power of God
   now the Holy Spirit lives within you.

357

Mick Gisbey
© 1985 Thankyou Music

1. **Have you got an appetite?**
   Do you eat what is right?
   Are you feeding on the Word of God?
   Are you fat or are you thin?
   Are you really full within?
   Do you find your strength in Him, or are you
       starving?

   You and me all should be exercising
       regularly,
   standing strong, all day long, giving God the
       glory.
   Feeding on the living bread, not eating
       crumbs but loaves instead;
   standing stronger, living longer, giving God
       the glory
   You and me all should be exercising regularly
   standing strong, all day long, giving God the
       glory.
   Feeding on the living bread, not eating
       crumbs but loaves instead;
   standing stronger, living longer, giving God
       the glory.

2. If it's milk or meat you need,
   why not have a slap-up feed,
   and stop looking like a weed and start to
       grow?
   Take the full fitness food,
   taste and see that God is good,

come on, feed on what you should and be
       healthy.
   You and me . . .
   giving God the, giving God the glory.

358

Ian Smale
© 1988 Glorie Music/Thankyou Music

Heavenly Father, we would sing out Your
    Praise,
You're everything a Father should be;
made us Your sons and daughters,
made us your own, children of God's family.

1. We older ones say, 'younger ones,
   we'll love and care for you.'
   We young ones say to older ones
   'our love respects you too.'
   We love you.
       Heavenly Father . . .

2. Father, as a family
   we will live forever.
   Your Church is made of all ages
   who love to be together.
   We love you.
       Heavenly Father . . .

359

Denis and Nan Allen
© 1988 Pilot Point Music/Lillenas Publishing
Co/Thanksgiving Music

1. **He made the water wet,**
   He made the land stay dry.
   He put twinkle in the stars
   and blue in the sky.
   And when He was sure
   it worked as it should,
   God looked at His world and said,
   'That's good!'

   Good, good, good! He said, 'That's good!'
   Good, good, good! God looked at His world
       and said,
   'That's good!'

2. He put a touch of wag
   in a puppy dog's tail,
   then put a little slow
   in a silly old snail.
   And when He was sure
   it worked as it should,
   God looked at His world and said,
   'That's good!'
       Good, good, good . . .

   That's good, that's good,
   (shouted) that's good!

360

Peter and Hanneke Jacobs
© 1988 Maranatha Music/Word Music (UK)

**He gives me strength, yes, He gives me
strength.**
I can do all things through Christ who gives
me strength.
Yes, He gives me strength, He gives me
strength.
I can do all things through Christ who gives
me strength.

361

Refrain: F. Whitfield
Copyright control

QUESTION **Hey, you (name) do you love
Jesus?**
ANSWER Yes, I love Jesus.
QUESTION Are you sure you love Jesus?
ANSWER Yes, I'm sure I love Jesus.
QUESTION Tell me, why do you love Jesus?
ANSWER This is why I love Jesus,
ALL because He first loved me.
Yes, I love Him, this is why I love Him.

All sing Oh, how I love Jesus.
Oh, how I love Jesus.
Oh, how I love Jesus,
because He first loved me.
Yes, I love Him, this is why I love Him.

362

Richard K. Avery and Donald S. Marsh
© 1967 by Hope Publishing Co

Hey! Hey! Anybody listening?
Hey! Hey! Anybody there?
Hey! Hey! Anybody listening?
Anybody care?

1. We've got good news, good news, good news,
good news:
Christ the Lord will soon be found here!
Good news, good news, good news, good
news:
let's help spread the news around here!
If I had a drum I'd drum it,
a mandolin I'd strum it,
a humming bird hum I'd hum it,
everywhere, everywhere, everywhere,
everywhere.
Hey! Hey! . . .

2. People come on, come on, come on, come on:
let's sing out for Mary's Son here!
Come on, come on, come on, come on:
He'll bring joy for everyone here!
If I had a harp I'd twang it,
a tambourine I'd bang it,
a fireman's bell I'd clang it,
everywhere, everywhere, everywhere,
everywhere.
Hey! Hey! . . .

3. Come on, sing out, sing out, sing out, sing out!
Tell the world about His birth now!
Sing out, sing out, sing out, sing out
loud and clear to all the earth now!
If I had a chime I'd ring it,
a finger cymbal ching it,
we've got this song let's sing it,
everywhere, everywhere, everywhere,
everywhere.
Hey! Hey! . . .

363

© 1989 Andy Silver

1. **His name was Saul of Tarsus,**
a clever Pharisee;
he studied Greek and Latin
and he spoke them fluently.
The only thing he wanted
was to wipe out those who said,
'We are followers of Jesus
and His truth we want to spread!'

Saul, Saul, Saul, Saul you're persecuting Me;
the Christians that you're killing are true
followers of Me.
Saul, Saul, Saul, Saul you really need to see
I came to bring forgiveness and to set all
people free.

2. Determined to pursue them
on his way he quickly strode,
heading for Damascus
along the well worn road.
The followers of Jesus
he wanted locked away,
but little did he know
that God would speak to him that day.
Saul, Saul, . . .

3. When God had finished speaking
Saul stood and tried to find
the men who had been with him,
but the light had made him blind.
They led him to a little house,
he stayed for just three days.
When he realised what had happened
he was simply quite amazed.
Saul, Saul, . . .

4. This brought about a change in Saul
he'd never be the same;
not only had his life been changed
he'd got a different name.
The Lord had given to Paul the task
to go to everyone,
and tell them that the way to God
is only through His Son.
Saul, Saul, . . .

364
Iain Craig

His ways are not our ways
but His ways are the best.
If we follow Jesus
we know that we'll be blessed.
If we trust Him He will help us,
listen when we pray.
His ways are not our ways
but His ways are the best.

1. When I call He listens, when I fall He's near.
   He has promised He will help me,
   I will never fear.
   His ways . . .

2. If I ever wander, if I turn from Him,
   He has promised He will help me,
   I will never fear.
   His ways . . .

3. He will always love me, He will always care.
   He has promised He will help me,
   I will never fear.
   His ways . . .

365
Carl Tuttle

1. **Hosanna, hosanna, hosanna in the highest;**
   hosanna, hosanna, hosanna in the highest.
   Lord, we lift up Your name,
   with hearts full of praise.
   Be exalted, O Lord my God—
   hosanna, in the highest.

2. Glory, glory, glory to the King of kings;
   glory, glory, glory to the King of kings.
   Lord, we lift up Your name,
   with hearts full of praise.
   Be exalted, O Lord my God—
   glory to the King of kings.

366

I am like a house with two windows and a
door
but underneath I have two legs that reach
down to the floor;
two ears to hear what's happening and a
thatched roof up above,
but right inside God's given me, a heart that's
full of love.
So jump up and turn around
and thank the Lord with joyful sound.
So jump up and turn around
and thank the Lord, and now sit down!

367
Richard K. Avery and Donald S. Marsh

I am the Church!—(With your thumb, point to
   yourself)
You are the Church!—(Point to your partner)
We are the Church together!—(Shake hands)
All who follow Jesus,—(Reach out with both
   hands)
all around the world,—(Circle arms over
   head)
yes we're the Church together.—(Link arms)

1. The Church is not a building, the Church is
   not a steeple.
   The Church is not a resting place, the Church
   is a people!
   I am the Church . . .

2. We're many kinds of people with many kinds
   of faces:
   all colours and all ages, too, from all times
   and places.
   I am the Church . . .

3. Sometimes the Church is marching,
   sometimes it's bravely burning,
   sometimes it's riding, sometimes hiding;
   always it's learning!
   I am the Church . . .

4. And when the people gather there's singing
   and there's praying,
   there's laughing and there's crying
   sometimes, all of it saying:
   I am the Church . . .

5. At Pentecost some people received the Holy
   Spirit
   and told the good news through the world to
   all who would hear it.
   I am the Church . . .

6. I count if I am ninety, or nine, or just a baby;
   there's one thing I am sure about and I don't
   mean maybe:
   I am the Church . . .

368
Peter and Hanneke Jacobs

I am the Resurrection and the Life.
I am the Resurrection and the Life.
He that believe in Me though he may die
yet shall he live again.
And whoever lives and believes in Me,
and whoever lives and believes in Me,
the Bible says in John eleven twenty five and
   twenty six
that we shall never die.

369
Kelly Willard
© 1978 Maranatha Music/Word Music (UK)

1. **I cast all my cares upon You.**
   I lay all of my burdens down at Your feet.
   And anything that I don't know what to do,
   I will cast all my cares upon You.

2. I cast all my cares upon You.
   I lay all of my burdens down at Your feet.
   And anytime that I don't know what to do,
   I will cast all of my cares upon You.
   I will cast all my cares upon You.

370
Susan Sayers
© 1986 Kevin Mayhew Ltd, licence no 191180

1. **I have a friend who is deeper than the
   ocean;**
   I have a friend who is wider than the sky.
   I have a friend who always understands me,
   whether I'm happy, or ready to cry.

2. If I am lost He will search until He finds me;
   if I am scared He will help me to be brave.
   All I've to do is to turn to Him and ask Him.
   I know He'll keep the promise He gave:

3. 'Don't be afraid,' said Jesus, 'I am with you'.
   'Don't be afraid,' said Jesus, 'I am here.
   Now and forever, anywhere you travel,
   I shall be with you, I'll always be near'.

371 © 1990 Greg Leavers

I look out through the doorway,
who's that I see before me?
My young son coming home.
I must run to meet him,
hug him when I greet him,
and say, 'Son, welcome home.'
We will have a party
and I can't wait to start.
He must have the very finest food,
the best robe, ring and sandals.
He was lost, but now is found.
Welcome home, son, welcome home.

372
Paul Crouch and David Mudie
© 1989 Daybreak Music Ltd

I love You Lord Jesus
the King of all things.
You love me Lord Jesus,
Your love never ends.
To You I am special,
Your promises are true.
You love me Lord Jesus,
and Lord I love You.

373
Anon
Copyright control

I am a sheep, baa, baa,
and I like to be well fed;
but like a sheep, baa, baa,
I'm a little stupid in the head.

I go astray most every day.
Oh what a trouble I must be.
I'm glad I've got the Good Shepherd (*spoken*)
looking after me, ha, ha, ha, ha, baa, baa.

374
Doug Holck
© 1981 Pilot Point Music/Lillenas Publishing Co/
Thankyou Music

1. **I want to love You, Lord;**
   I want to serve You, Lord;
   I want to please You, Lord;
   this is my prayer.

2. I want to love You, Lord;
   I want to serve You, Lord;
   I want to please You, Lord;
   this is my prayer.

375 © 1990 Greg Leavers

1. **I want to tell you (I want to tell you)**
   my eyes are blue (my eyes are blue),
   I want to show you (I want to show you)
   what I can do (*clap! clap!*) (what I can do)
   (*clap! clap!*).

   *There's no-one, not one, in the world like me.
   I'm so very, very, very, very special you see.
   There's no-one, not one, in the world like me,
   for God made me just the way He wanted me
   to be.*

2. There are so many (there are so many)
   things I can do (things I can do).
   I don't feel useless (I don't feel useless)
   these words are true (these words are true).
   There's no-one . . .

3. Jesus is special (Jesus is special),
   I'm special too (I'm special too).
   He says He loves me (He says He loves me)
   and He loves you (and He loves you).
   There's no-one . . .

376
Ian Smale
© 1985 Glorie Music/Thankyou Music

**I will wave my hands in praise and
   adoration;**
I will wave my hands in praise and adoration;
I will wave my hands in praise and adoration;
praise and adoration to the living God.

For He's given me hands that just love
   clapping—
one, two, one, two, three—

and He's given me a voice that just loves
    shouting
Hallelujah!

He's given me feet that just love dancing—
one, two, one, two, three—
and He's put me in a being that has no
    trouble seeing
that whatever I am feeling He is worthy to be
    praised.

377

I'm a footstep follower
for Jesus leads the way.
He knows the life that's best for me:
a plan for every day.
As I walk and talk with Him,
He'll never let me stray.
I'm a footstep follower
for Jesus leads the way.

378

**I'm going to hide God's Word inside my
    heart**
and learn each verse from memory.
I'm going to hide God's Word inside my heart
until His Word is part of me.

God's Word will help me each and every day
to know what is right from what is wrong.
The more that I read it, the more I learn of
    Him,
and His Word will make me strong.

That's why I'm going to hide God's Word
    inside my heart
and learn each verse from memory.
I'm going to hide God's Word inside my heart
until His Word is part of me,
until His Word is part of me.

379

I'm going to say my prayers,
read my Bible every morning;
going to get some fellowship,
witness every day.
I'm going to say my prayers,
read my Bible every morning;
going to get some fellowship,
witness every day.

1. I am going to pray every morning,
   I am going to pray every day.
   I am going to pray every morning,
   I am going to pray every day.
     I'm going to say . . .

2. I am going to read my Bible every morning,
   I am going to read my Bible every day.
   I am going to read my Bible every morning,
   I am going to read my Bible every day.
     I'm going to say . . .

3. I am going to fellowship every morning,
   I am going to fellowship every day.
   I am going to fellowship every morning,
   I am going to fellowship every day.
     I'm going to say . . .

4. I am going to witness every morning,
   I am going to witness every day.
   I am going to witness every morning,
   I am going to witness every day.
     I'm going to say . . .

380

**I'm going to stand up, I'm going to stand
    up,**
I'm going to stand up, I'm going to stand up.

I'm going to stand up, stand up and live for
    Jesus,
Oo I, I'm going to stand up, stand up and live
    for Him.
I'm going to give up, give up my life for
    Jesus,
Oo I, I'm going to give up, give up my life for
    Him.

Lord we will live our lives for You,
serve You faithfully, like You want us to.
Lord, You give us the power to live for You,
live for You.

I'm going to stand up . . .

Let's take a stand for Jesus,
let's live our lives for Jesus.
Let's give it all for Jesus.
Stand up for Jesus! Stand up for Jesus!
Stand up, stand up, stand up, stand up,
    stand up!

I'm going to stand up . . .

I'm going to stand up, I'm going to stand up,
I'm going to stand up, I'm going to stand up.
Stand up!

381

1. **I'm going to take** (*clap clap*)**, a step of faith**,
   I'm going to put my trust in the Lord.
   He has the power to carry me through.
   If I listen carefully, He'll tell me what to do.
   I'm going to take (*clap clap*) a step of faith,
   and put my trust in the Lord.

2. I'm going to take (*clap clap*) a step of faith,
I'm going to put my trust in the Lord.
He made a promise, He loves me so;
wherever He might lead me, He'll never let
    me go.
I'm going to take (*clap clap*) a step of faith,
and put my trust in the Lord.

382 © 1992 Greg Leavers

I'm going to set my heart
on the precious Word of God;
I'm going to feed my heart
on His many promises.
His word helps me in trouble,
it teaches me to praise.
I don't want to live with a hungry heart;
I'm going to feed on the Word of God.

383 © 1992 Gillian E. Hutchinson·

1. **I've come to a time when I must change,**
a time when I have to choose,
to order my own life, or follow Christ,
and gain what I cannot lose.

    My Lord, I come,
    I'm giving my life to You.
    Fill me with Your Spirit,
    and make over my heart anew.

2. The ways of the past, I leave, I leave,
my life in His hands I place.
His strength will uphold me through anything,
sufficient for me His grace.
    My Lord . . .

3. The wrong that I've done, I now confess,
I know that He will forgive.
His love is far greater than all my sin,
He'll teach me the way to live.
    My Lord . . .

4. From love of myself, I turn, I turn,
to serving the King of kings.
My life will be filled with the love of Christ,
whatever the future brings.
    My Lord . . .

5. I've come to a time when I must change,
a time when I have to choose,
to order my own life, or follow Christ,
and gain what I cannot lose.

384 Terrye Coelho
© 1973 Maranatha! Music/Word Music (UK)

If any man come after Me, let him deny
    himself,
pick up his cross and follow Me into life
    eternally.

Deny yourself, pick up your cross, and follow
    Jesus.
He is the Way, Truth, and Life.

Optional 2nd part

Alleluia! Praise the Lord, worship Him in one
    accord.
Alleluia! He is King, Master, Lord of
    everything.
Jesus Christ, Lord of all, loving great and
    small;
He is the Way, Truth, and Life.

385 © 1992 Gillian E. Hutchinson

1. **If it pleases the King,**
I want to live my life for Him.
If it offers Him praise,
I will follow His ways.
Sinful I may be,
but He will welcome me.
My life to Him I'll bring,
if it pleases the King.

2. If it pleases the King,
I want to give my love to Him.
If it honours the Lord,
I will trust in His Word.
I need never fear,
for He'll be ever near.
My love to Him I'll sing,
if it pleases the King.

386 Sam Horner
© 1991 Daybreak Music Ltd

1. **If Jesus is de vine, we must be de**
    branches.
If Jesus is de vine, we must be de branches.
If Jesus is de vine, we must be de branches,
and bear fruit in the Kingdom of God.

2. If Jesus is de rock, we should be a little
    boulder.
If Jesus is de rock, we should be a little
    boulder.
If Jesus is de rock, we should be a little
    boulder,
to bear fruit in the Kingdom of God.

3. If Jesus is de bread, is your name on the roll
    now?
If Jesus is de bread, is your name on the roll
    now?
If Jesus is de bread, is your name on the roll
    now?
Let's bear fruit in the Kingdom of God.

387 © 1991 Andy Hughes

***If you love Me you will obey My
commandments.***
*If you love Me you will do what I say;
and if you love Me then every day you will
seek Me
saying, 'Lord what shall I do today?'*

1. Just like Joshua
standing at the Jordan's side;
obeyed the Lord and when he started to
cross
the waters opened wide.
   If you love Me . . .

2. As the disciples
obeyed and brought Him fish and bread.
So Jesus blessed it and they handed it round
and five thousand men were fed.
   If you love Me . . .

388 Derek Llewellyn
© 1989 Sea Dream Music

1. **If you climb** *(stamp stamp)* **to the top of a
mountain,**
   if you swim *(splish splish)* in the ocean blue,
   if you're lost *(sniff sniff)* in the deepest forest,
   Jesus will always find you.

2. If you fall *(scream)* into the darkest cave,
   if you fly *(zoom)* right up into the air,
   if you run *(run on the spot)* all around the world,
   Jesus will always be there.

3. So if you're feeling lonely,
   if you're feeling sad,
   Jesus will always be close to you,
   so you can always feel glad.

4. If you climb *(stamp stamp)* to the top of a
mountain,
   if you swim *(splish splish)* in the ocean blue,
   if you're lost *(sniff sniff)* in the deepest forest,
   Jesus will always find you.

389 Michael Ryan
© 1975 Maranatha! Music/Word Music (UK)

If you want to be great in God's kingdom,
learn to be the servant of all.
If you want to be great in God's kingdom,
learn to be the servant of all.
Learn to be the servant of all,
learn to be the servant of all.
If you want to be great in God's kingdom,
learn to be the servant of all.

390 Anon
Copyright control

If your empty tum is rumbling
you don't leave your baked beans *(munch
munch).*
If it's lightning and it's thundering
you don't stand beneath the trees.
And if you climb a high steep hill
you don't refuse a Coke *(pshhh).*
And if your best friend's feeling ill
you don't treat it like a joke *(ha ha).*
You don't run across the high street
if you want to grow old.
You don't look down at your feet
if you want to score a goal *(clap clap).*
So don't forget to pray
if you want to follow God today.
You don't put your Bible out of sight
if you want to do what's right.
You don't put your Bible out of sight,
if you want to do what's right.

391 Ian White
© Little Misty Music Ltd

**In everything that I do, show me what
Jesus would do.**
In everything that I do, show me what Jesus
would do.
I will not be afraid, for I can always pray,
show me what Jesus would do.

392 Alan J. Price
© 1990 Daybreak Music Ltd

I'm going to shine, shine, shine,
*a light in the world I'll be;
I want to shine, shine, shine,
let people see Jesus in me!*

1. I want to glorify the Father
   by the things I do;
   be the person God has made me,
   letting His love flow through!
   I'm going to . . .

2. And when it's hard and it's not so easy
   to know and do what's right;
   I'll trust the Holy Spirit in me,
   to help me win each fight!
   I'm going to . . .

3. Even if I fail Him often
   and my light is dim;
   He has promised to forgive me,
   I can come back to Him!
   I'm going to . . .

393
Marjorie Allen Anderson
© 1947 Scripture Press Foundation

1. **In the morning when I rise,**
   when I open up my eyes,
   rain or shine or cold and ice,
   God is near, God is near.

2. When I help and when I play,
   He is there to show the way,
   close behind me all the day,
   God is near, God is near.

3. Then when I turn off the light,
   when I go to sleep at night,
   I am always in His sight,
   God is near, God is near.

394
Harry D. Clarke
© 1924 Hope Publishing Company

1. Into my heart, into my heart,
   come into my heart, Lord Jesus.
   Come in today, come in to stay;
   come into my heart, Lord Jesus.

2. Rule in my heart, rule in my heart,
   O King of my heart, Lord Jesus,
   Make this Your throne, rule there alone;
   O King of my heart, Lord Jesus.

395
Ian White
© Little Misty Music Ltd

*It takes an almighty hand, to make your
   harvest grow.
It takes an almighty hand, however you may
   sow.
It takes an almighty hand, the world around
   me shows.
It takes the almighty hand of God.*

1. It takes His hand to grow your garden,
   all from a secret in a seed;
   part of a plan He spoke and started,
   and said is 'very good indeed!'
   It takes . . .

2. It takes His hand to turn the seasons,
   to give the sun and snow their hour;
   and in this plan we learn His reason,
   His nature and eternal power.
   It takes . . .

3. It took His hands to carry sorrow,
   for every sin that we have done;
   and on a cross He bought tomorrow,
   a world of good, like He'd begun.
   It takes . . .

4. And in His hands there is perfection,
   that in this land we only taste;
   for now we see a poor reflection,
   then we shall see Him face to face.
   It takes . . .

396
Joy Webb
© Salvationist Publishing & Supplies Ltd

1. **It was on a starry night when the hills were
      bright,**
   earth lay sleeping, sleeping calm and still;
   then in a cattle shed, in a manger bed
   a Boy was born, King of all the world.

   *And all the angels sang for Him,
   the bells of heaven rang for Him;
   for a Boy was born, King of all the world.
   And all the angels sang for Him,
   the bells of heaven rang for Him;
   for a Boy was born, King of all the world.*

2. Soon the shepherds came that way, where
      the Baby lay,
   and were kneeling, kneeling by His side.
   And their hearts believed again, for the
      peace of men
   for a Boy was born, King of all the world.
   And all the angels . . .

   On a starry night, on a starry night.

397
© 1989 Andy Silver

1. **It was Jesus who taught His disciples,**
   it was Jesus who called them by name.
   Then one night on the lake came the wind
      and the rain,
   and the waves splashed right over the boat.

   *Splish, splash, pitter pitter pat,
   down came the storm with a bang and a
      crash.
   Splish, splash, pitter pitter pat,
   down came the storm with a bang and a
      crash.*

2. It was Jesus asleep in the trawler,
   it was Jesus who woke to their cries.
   'Don't you care that we drown, we're afraid
      we'll go down!'
   and the waves splashed right over the boat.
   Splish splash . . .

3. It was Jesus who stood to attention,
   it was Jesus who spoke to the waves.
   'You be quiet do no harm'; right away there
      was calm.
   'Who's this man?' asked the men in the boat.
   Splish splash . . .

398
© 1991 Greg Leavers

It's a song of praise,
*it's a song of thankfulness;
it's a song of joy,
for every girl and boy.*

1. God gave me my hands,
   God gave me my voice;
   God gave me a thankful heart,
   so now I can rejoice.
      It's a song of praise . . .

2. God gave me my feet,
   God gave me my arms;
   the life and love He gives to me
   makes me want to dance.
      It's a song of praise . . .

399

Alan J. Price
© 1990 Daybreak Music Ltd

It's an adventure following Jesus,
it's an adventure learning of Him.
It's an adventure living for Jesus,
it's an adventure following Him.
Let's go where He leads us,
turn away from wrong;
for we know we can trust Him
to help us as we go along.

It's an adventure following Jesus,
it's an adventure learning of Him.
It's an adventure living for Jesus,
it's an adventure following Him.

400

Paul Crouch and David Mudie
© 1989 Daybreak Music Ltd

It's easy to be a believer,
because it's plain as plain can be
that Jesus came from God and went
to die at Calvary.
But three days later He rose up
and was seen by at least five hundred
      people,
and then went back to heaven
to sit at God's right hand.

401

© 1992 Greg Leavers

**It's not very nice saying 'Na na na na na
   na';**
it's not very good saying 'It's not fair'.
It's not very kind to fight your sister or your
   brother,
or to sneer at others saying 'I don't care'.

God doesn't like these things—
He tells us in the Bible they're called sins;
God doesn't like these things.
We do it (*Uh huh*), we know it (*That's right*),
and we need help to stop it.

402

Basil Bridge
© Oxford University Press

1. **It's rounded like an orange,**
   this earth on which we stand;
   and we praise the God who holds it
   in the hollow of His hand.

   *So Father, we would thank You
      for all that You have done,
   and for all that You have given us
      through the coming of Your Son.*

2. A candle, burning brightly,
   can cheer the darkest night
   and these candles tell how Jesus
   came to bring a dark world light.
      So Father . . .

3. The ribbon round the orange
   reminds us of the cost;
   how the Shepherd, strong and gentle,
   gave His life to save the lost.
      So Father . . .

4. Four seasons with their harvest
   supply the food we need,
   and the Spirit gives a harvest
   that can make us rich indeed.
      So Father . . .

5. We come with our Christingles
   to tell of Jesus' birth
   and we praise the God who blessed us
   by His coming to this earth.
      So Father . . .

403

Boyd Bacon
© 1988 Lillenas Publishing Co/Thankyou Music

1. **It's the little things that show our love for
   Jesus.**
   It's the little things that show our love for Him.
   It's in little things that we can truly serve Him.
   It's with little things that we begin.

   *Give a little more love and a little more hope
      to others as you serve Him.
   Give a little more love and a little more hope
      to others you may meet.
   Give a little more love each day to those
      around you.
   Then a little more love and a little more faith,
   and a little more love and a little more faith
      will make you more like Him.*

2. It's the little things we do each day for others.
   It's the little things that show we really care.
   It's in little things our faith becomes much
      stronger.
   It's with little things that we begin.

Give a little more love and a little more hope
  to others as you serve Him.
Give a little more love and a little more hope
  to others you may meet.
Give a little more love each day to those
  around you.
Then a little more love and a little more faith,
and a little more love and a little more faith,
and a little more love and a little more faith,
and a little more love and a little more faith
  will make you more like Him.
I want to be more like Him, more like Him.

404
Ian Smale
© 1987 Glorie Music/Thankyou Music

Jehovah Jireh, God will provide.
Jehovah Rophe, God heals.
Jehovah Makeddesh, God who sanctifies.
Jehovah Nissi, God is my banner.
Jehovah Rohi, God my shepherd.
Jehovah Shalom, God is peace.
Jehovah Tsidkenu, God our righteousness.
Jehovah Shammah, God who is there.

405
© 1989 Andy Silver

1. **Jerusalem man, walking from his homeland,**
   when he fell among some robbers, poor
     Jerusalem man.
   They stripped him and they beat him with
     their sticks in their hands;
   poor, poor, poor, poor Jerusalem man.
2. They hastily fled as he fell down and bled,
   but a man who was a preacher saw the victim
     ahead.
   He passed him and ignored him—not a word
     had been said;
   poor, poor, poor, poor Jerusalem man.
3. Along came a man who was very well read,
   now he must have seen the victim who by
     now was half dead.
   He passed him and ignored him—not a word
     had been said;
   poor, poor, poor, poor Jerusalem man.
4. The next man to pass, a Samaritan man,
   though he always had been taught to hate a
     true Jewish man,
   he helped him and he took him to an inn near
     his land;
   good, good, good, good Samaritan man.

406
Scott Lawrence
© Copyright Control

Jesus has promised my Shepherd to be,
that's why I love Him so;
and to the children He said, 'Come to Me',
that's why I love Him so.

That's why I love Him, that's why I love Him,
because He first loved me;
when I'm tempted and tried, He is close by
    my side
that's why I love Him so.

407
© Timothy Dudley-Smith

1. **Jesus, Prince and Saviour,**
   Lord of life who died;
   Christ, the friend of sinners,
   sinners crucified.
   For a lost world's ransom,
   all Himself He gave,
   lay at last death's victim,
   lifeless in the grave.

   Lord of life triumphant,
   risen now to reign!
   King of endless ages,
   Jesus lives again!

2. In His power and Godhead
   every victory won,
   pain and passion ended,
   all His purpose done:
   Christ the Lord is risen!
   sighs and sorrows past,
   death's dark night is over,
   morning comes at last!
     Lord of life . . .

3. Resurrection morning!
   sinners' bondage freed.
   Christ the Lord is risen—
   He is risen indeed!
   Jesus, Prince and Saviour,
   Lord of life who died,
   Christ the King of glory
   now is glorified!
     Lord of life . . .

408
Graham Kendrick
© 1986 Thankyou Music

1. **Jesus put this song into our hearts,**
   Jesus put this song into our hearts;
   it's a song of joy no-one can take away.
   Jesus put this song into our hearts.

2. Jesus taught us how to live in harmony,
   Jesus taught us how to live in harmony;
   different faces, different races,
     He made us one—
   Jesus taught us how to live in harmony.

3. Jesus taught us how to be a family,
   Jesus taught us how to be a family;
   loving one another
     with the love that He gives—
   Jesus taught us how to be a family.

4. Jesus turned our sorrow into dancing,
   Jesus turned our sorrow into dancing;
   changed our tears of sadness
      into rivers of joy—
   Jesus turned our sorrow into a dance. *Hey!*

409
Derek Llewellyn
© 1991 Sea Dream Music

**Jesus, send me the helper, send me the
   helper to help me.**
Jesus, send me the Holy Spirit, send the Holy
   Spirit to me.
Jesus, send me the helper, send me the
   helper to help me.
Jesus, send me the Holy Spirit, send the Holy
   Spirit to me.

He gives us love to keep on loving.
He makes us brave to do what is right.
He gives us faith to keep on going.
He gives us power to keep us shining so
   bright.

Jesus, send me the helper, send me the
   helper to help me.
Jesus, send me the Holy Spirit, send the Holy
   Spirit to me.

410
Ottis Skillings
© 1984 Lillenas Publishing Co/Thankyou Music

1. **Jesus, I love You, love You, love You.**
   Jesus, I love You; Jesus, my Lord.

2. Jesus, I serve You, serve You, serve You.
   Jesus, I serve You; Jesus, my Lord.

3. Jesus, I praise You, praise You, praise You.
   Jesus, I praise You; Jesus, my Lord;
   Jesus, my Lord.

411
J. Watson
© Scripture Union

1. **Jesus was the Son of God,**
   He became a man.
   He was strong and good and kind,
   followed all God's plan
   followed all God's plan.

2. When He was a strong young man
   Jesus had to die.
   All his friends were very sad,
   and they wondered why,
   and they wondered why.

3. It's so hard to understand
   why this had to be;
   but I know it was because
   He cared for you and me,
   He cared for you and me.

412
© 1990 Greg Leavers

Jesus will never, ever,
no not ever, never, ever change.
He will always, always,
that's for all days,
always be the same.
So as Son of God and
King of kings
He will forever reign.
Yesterday, today, forever,
Jesus is the same.
Yesterday, today, forever,
Jesus is the same.

413
© S. and J. Doddridge

Joseph was sold as a slave,
and later was thrown into prison;
but God helped him be very brave,
because he had done nothing wrong.
For God knows, yes God knows, God knows
   the truth;
for God knows, yes God knows, God knows
   the truth.

414
Gloria Gaither and Gary S. Paxton
© 1978/1988 Gaither Music Company/United
Nations Music Publishing Ltd/Boosey & Hawkes
Music Publishers Ltd

Kids under construction;
maybe the paint is still wet.
Kids under construction;
the Lord might not be finished yet.

1. We're more than just accidents without the
      cause;
   we're more than just bodies and brains.
   God made us on purpose, we're part of a
      plan;
   He cares and He knows us by name. Oh!
      Kids under construction . . .

2. Now, mister, I know that I get in your way;
   I'm noisy and just bug you so.
   But there's lots of questions I just have to ask
   if I'm ever going to know. Oh!
      Kids under construction . . .

3. Dear Jesus, please make us more patient and
      kind;
   and help us to be more like You.
   And make room for all other children of
      Yours,
   for they are still growing up, too. Oh!
      Kids under construction . . .

415

David Matthews
© 1975 Word Music (UK)

1. **Large creatures, small creatures,**
   short and tall creatures,
   come now and praise the Lord.
   Young creatures, old creatures,
   hot and cold creatures,
   come now and praise the Lord.

   *Sing praise to the Father, sing praise to the
      Son,
   sing praise to the Spirit who makes all
      creatures one.
   Sing praise for the goodness of what the Lord
      has done.
   Let all creatures praise the Lord.*

2. Low creatures, high creatures,
   flying in the sky creatures,
   come now and praise the Lord.
   White creatures, brown creatures,
   all the world around creatures,
   come now and praise the Lord.
      Sing praise . . .

3. Day creatures, night creatures,
   left and right creatures,
   come now and praise the Lord.
   Near creatures, far creatures,
   anywhere you are creatures,
   come now and praise the Lord.
      Sing praise . . .

416

© 1992 Greg Leavers

**Let's go and tell our friends that Jesus
      cares;**
let's go and tell our friends that Jesus cares.
We've got to go out and tell how Jesus died
      for them;
to tell them how He loves them (*that's right!*);
to tell them He'll forgive them (*that's true!*);
to tell them He'll be with them (*Amen*);
to tell them that He wants to be their friend.

417

Alison Moon
© 1992 Daybreak Music Ltd

Let's praise God together,
*let us clap and praise the Lord;
for He loves to hear us—
He is King for evermore..*

1. Jesus, holy is Your name;
   high above all others,
   power and glory belong to You.

   *Let's all dance together,
   let us dance and praise the Lord;
   for he loves to see us—
   He is King for evermore.*

2. Jesus, mighty is Your name;
   high above all others,
   power and glory belong to You.

   *Let's praise God together,
   let us clap and praise the Lord;
   for He loves to hear us—
   He is King for evermore.*

   *Let's all dance together,
   let us dance and praise the Lord;
   for he loves to see us—
   He is King for evermore.*

418

Anon
Copyright control

1. **Long ago there was born, in the city of
      David,**
   a sweet, holy Babe who was Jesus, our King.
   Angels sang at His birth, 'Lullaby, peace on
      earth.'
   Angels sang at His birth, 'Lullaby, peace on
      earth.'

2. Jesus came as a child from His Father in
      heaven,
   and has shown us the way to be loving and
      kind.
   While the stars sang above, 'Lullaby, God is
      love.'
   While the stars sang above, 'Lullaby, God is
      love.'

419

© 1989 Andy Silver

1. **Long, long ago before our time began**
   everything was out of shape and nothing
      filled the land.
   God, who saw the emptiness made a plan to
      clear the mess,
   God spoke and it was done.
   Day one, came the light and the day and night;
   day two, came the clouds and the sea and sky;
   day three, came the land and the plants and
      trees;
   day four, came the sun and the moon and the
      stars.

2. God took a look and He was happy and was
      pleased.
   Now the world was taking shape and all
      because God breathed;
   but He thought the sky and sea needed some
      activity—
   God spoke and it was done.
   Day five, came the fish and the birds that fly;
   day six, came the beasts and the animals;
   and then came the people called Adam and Eve;
   day seven, all was done and God rested at
      ease.

3. God was very glad to see the different forms
   of life,
   but the part most wonderful was Adam and
   his wife.
   All He wanted them to do was love and serve
   Him through and through;
   God spoke and it was done.

420
Bev Gammon
© 1989 Thankyou Music

1. **Lord Jesus**
   You are faithful,
   always with us,
   never leaving us;
   Lord Jesus.

2. Lord Jesus
   You are blameless,
   You are perfect,
   You are sinless;
   Lord Jesus.

3. Lord Jesus
   You are so pure,
   pure and lovely,
   pure and holy;
   Lord Jesus.

421
Paul Field
© 1983 Waif/Heath Leoy Music

1. **Lord, make me a mountain standing tall for
   You;**
   strong and free and holy, in everything I do.
   Lord, make me a river of water pure and sweet.
   Lord, make me the servant of everyone I meet.

2. Lord, make me a candle shining with Your
   light;
   steadfastly unflickering, standing for the right.
   Lord, make me a fire burning strong for You.
   Lord, make me be humble in everything I do.

3. Lord, make me a mountain, strong and tall for
   You;
   Lord, make me a fountain of water clear and
   new.
   Lord, make me a shepherd that I may feed
   Your sheep.
   Lord, make me the servant of everyone I meet.

422
Ian Smale
© 1989 Glorie Music/Thankyou Music

Lord, we've come to worship You;
Lord, we've come to praise.
Lord, we've come to worship You
in oh, so many ways.
Some of us shout and some of us sing,
and some of us whisper the praise we bring;
but Lord, we all are gathering
to give to You our praise.

423
© 1991 Greg Leavers

1. **Lord, You are brilliant, champion of
   champions;**
   to You our thanks and praise we bring.
   You made all the world, no-one's as great as
   You;
   You know everything and all Your words are
   true.
   Lord, You are brilliant, champion of
   champions;
   so we proclaim You are the King.

2. Lord, You are brilliant, champion of
   champions;
   to You our thanks and praise we bring.
   You see everything, all that we say and do;
   You're incredible, no-one loves us like You.
   Lord, You are brilliant, champion of
   champions;
   so we proclaim You are the King.

424
© 1988 Fiona Inkpen

*Lord, You are the Light of the World, shine
in our hearts.*
*Let that light shine across the earth, Light of
the World, our God.*

1. In the warmth of Your love we would walk in
   Your light.
   Lord, You are . . .

2. Midst the sorrow of man may Your love fill our
   hearts.
   Lord, You are . . .

3. Lord, the Truth and the life, revealing Your
   way!
   Lord, You are . . .

425
Peter and Hanneke Jacobs
© 1988 Maranatha! Music/Word Music (UK)

Love, joy, peace,
patience, kindness, goodness, faith,
gentleness, and self control;
this is the fruit of the Spirit.
Love, joy, peace,
patience, kindness, goodness, faith,
gentleness and self control;
the fruit of the Spirit of God.

You'll find it in Galatians, chapter five,
verse twenty-two.
And if you're walking close to God,
this fruit will grow in you.

And you'll have love, joy, peace,
patience, kindness, goodness, faith,
gentleness, and self control;
this is the fruit of the Spirit.
Love, joy, peace,
patience, kindness, goodness, faith,
gentleness and self control;
the fruit of the Spirit of God.
The fruit of the Spirit of God.

426 © 1992 Gillian E. Hutchinson

1. **M-m-m-m-must I really go and visit him?**
   I'd n-not be very good at it, you know.
   Surely there's s-someone else who's w-w-
       willing to;
   I'm a-f-f-fraid to go!

2. He's been p-p-persecuting Your followers,
   some have been k-killed, and some were
       thrown in jail.
   Please d-d-don't make me go and v-v-visit
       him;
   I'll be sh-sh-sure to fail.

   Listen Ananias, I've chosen this man
   to be a witness for Me.
   Through him, the good news will spread to
       many nations,
   bringing life and liberty.

3. If I really must, Lord, I'll be o-b-bedient;
   I know You'll go with me, You'll s-see me
       through.
   Even when the task is hard or d-d-dangerous,
   help me to t-trust in You.

427 Graham Kendrick
© 1986 Thankyou Music

1. **Make way, make way,**
   for Christ the King in splendour arrives;
   fling wide the gates
   and welcome Him into your lives.

   Make way, make way,
   for the King of kings;
   make way, make way,
   and let His kingdom in!

2. He comes the broken hearts to heal,
   the prisoners to free;
   the deaf shall hear, the lame shall dance,
   the blind shall see.
     Make way . . .

3. And those who mourn with heavy hearts,
   who weep and sigh,
   with laughter, joy and royal crown
   He'll beautify.
     Make way . . .

4. We call you now to worship Him
   as Lord of all;
   to have no gods before Him,
   their thrones must fall!
     Make way . . .

428 © 1990 Andy Silver

1. **Matthew had been sitting in his little hut,**
   collecting lots of money from the Jews.
   He had a reputation, dealing in deception,
   working for the Inland Revenue.
   Jesus had been walking on the shore that
       day,
   and called out 'Matthew come and follow Me!'
   There was no hesitation, he didn't even
       question,
   he left his hut and followed straight away.

   Come let's have a party,
   come and meet the Lord who called and
       found me;
   bring your friends and neighbours to the
       party.
   Come let's have a P.A.R.T.Y.

2. Jesus heard the whispers from the Pharisees,
   'See Him eating with these wicked men'.
   They didn't stop complaining, gossiping and
       jeering,
   thinking they were holy, righteous men.
   Jesus spoke directly to the Pharisees:
   'What sort of people need a doctor's help?
   The healthy do not need him, but people sick
       and ailing;
   I've come to call all sinners to repent!'
     Come let's have . . .

429 Carol Gaddy
© 1980 Lillenas Publishing Co/Thankyou Music

1. **Maybe you can't draw or sing or be a**
       football star;
   but just remember, be yourself,
   He made you like you are.

   It'll be a big thing when Jesus takes control,
   even though it seems like something very
       slim.
   From a tiny lunch He blessed the bread and
       fed the multitudes;
   and He'll use us, too, when we give ourselves
       to Him.

2. You may not have the brightest smile or make
       the highest score;
   but if you give Him what you have,
   He'll make it something more.
     It'll be a big . . .

3. If you love our blessed Lord and want to do
       your part,
   don't worry if you've nothing else—
   the best gift is your heart.
       It'll be a big . . .

430 Mavis Ford
© 1984 Springtide/Word Music (UK)

Mighty in victory, glorious in majesty:
every eye shall see Him when He appears,
coming in the clouds with power and glory.
   Hail to the King!
We must be ready, watching and praying,
serving each other, building His kingdom;
then every knee shall bow, then every tongue
       confess,
   Jesus is Lord!

431 Eugene Greco
© 1989 Integrity's Hosanna! Music

Mighty is our God,
mighty is our King.
Mighty is our Lord,
ruler of everything.
Glory to our God,
glory to our King.
Glory to our Lord,
ruler of everything.

His name is higher,
higher than any other name.
His power is greater,
for He has created* everything.

Mighty is our God . . .

*throw arm up in the air

432 © Peter Lewis

Noah was the only good man;
Noah was the only good man;
Noah was the only good man,
and everyone else was bad.

1. The Lord looked at the world He made
   and He was very sad,
   as almost everyone He saw
   was wicked and was bad.
   So God said He would send a flood
   to wash them all away,
   and He said, 'Noah, build an ark
   to float upon the waves!'
       Noah was . . .

2. So Noah built a wooden ark
   the way God told him to,
   and took his family safe inside
   with animals two by two.
   So God saved Noah from the flood

and promised then and there
that He would never send again
a flood upon the earth.
   Noah was . . .

3. God made a rainbow in the sky
   of yellow, blue and red,
   so no-one ever would forget
   the flood and what He said.
   And when we see the rainbow now
   remember God's own words:
   that He would never send again
   a flood upon the earth.
       Noah was . . .

433 © 1992 Gillian E. Hutchinson

1. **Now Saul was rejected as king of the land,**
   so God spoke to Samuel, 'Now hear my
       command.
   Go straight down to Bethlehem, there worship
       Me;
   anoint one of Jesse's sons as king to be!'

2. Now all Jesse's family were handsome and
       strong,
   and when Samuel asked them, they all came
       along;
   and Samuel was wondering as in they all trod,
   which one of the brothers was chosen by God.

3. He looked on Eliab, and he was impressed
   with the curls of his hair and the breadth of
       his chest;
   but God said to Samuel, 'That's not where I
       start—
   you look on his body, but I see his heart!'

4. So six more fine offspring of Jesse's passed
       by
   but each was rejected by God the Most High;
   then Samuel asked Jesse, 'Are those all
       you've got?'
   He answered, 'There's David—the babe of
       the lot!'

5. Now David, the shepherd, the youngest of
       eight,
   was out with the sheep on the hills until late.
   He had to be sent for; and when he came in,
   the Lord said, 'Rise up and anoint him as
       king!'

6. You may be dressed smartly, your face may
       be fair,
   but God's not concerned with your clothes or
       your hair;
   your outward appearance is only a part—
   when God looks upon you, He looks on your
       heart.

434
Joanne Pond
© 1980 Thankyou Music

O give thanks to the Lord,
all you His people;
O give thanks to the Lord,
 for He is good.
Let us praise, let us thank,
let us celebrate and dance;
O give thanks to the Lord,
 for He is good.

435
Ian Smale
© 1985 Glorie Music/Thankyou Music

1. **O Lord, You're great, You are fabulous.**
 We love you more than any words can sing,
  sing, sing.
 O Lord, You're great, You are so generous;
 You lavish us with gifts when we don't
  deserve a thing.

 Allelu, alleluia, praise You Lord.
 Alleluia, praise You Lord, alleluia, praise You
  Lord.
 Allelu, alleluia, praise You Lord.
 Alleluia, praise You Lord, alleluia, praise You
  Lord.

2. O Lord, You're great, You are so powerful;
 You hold the mighty universe in Your hand,
  hand, hand.
 O Lord, You're great, You are so wonderful,
 You've poured out Your love on this
  undeserving land.
  Allelu, alleluia . . .

436
Kurt Kaiser
© 1975 Word Music Inc (a division of Word Inc
USA)/Word Music (UK)

1. **Oh, how He loves you and me;**
 oh, how He loves you and me.
 He gave His life—
 what more could He give?

 Oh, how He loves you;
 oh, how He loves me;
 oh, how He loves you and me.

2. Jesus to Calvary did go,
 His love for sinners to show.
 What He did there
 brought hope from despair.
  Oh, how He . . .

437
© 1991 Greg Leavers

Oh no! The wine's all gone!
How can the wedding feast now go on?
Oh dear! What can be done?
Just listen to Jesus, Mary's Son.
Oh yes! We'll do what He says—

fill the stone jars with water that's fresh.
Oh my! They're pouring it out!
What, wine? That's the miracle! without a
 doubt!

438
Angela Flynn
© 1989 Sea Dream Music

1. **Oh, oh, oh, oh.**
 Oh, oh, oh, oh.

2. Hallelujah, hallelujah.
 Halleluja, hallelujah.

3. Christ died and rose. He will come again.
 Christ died and rose. He will come again.

4. Praise the Lord.
 Praise the Lord.

439
Sam Horner
© 1992 Daybreak Music Ltd

Oh yes I am, oh yes I am,
I am saved and kept secure in Jesus' hand.
Oh yes I am, oh yes I am,
I am saved and kept secure in Jesus' hand.

1. I'm redeemed, the price was paid by Him;
 justified, just as if I'd never sinned;
 sanctified, holy, set apart;
 and it's all because of Jesus' loving heart.
  Oh yes I am . . .

2. I am saved, from death and sin and hell.
 I'm empowered, by the Spirit of God as well.
 I'm born again, I've got a brand new start;
 and it's all because of Jesus' loving heart.
  Oh yes I am . . .

3. I belong to my Father who's above.
 I am kept by His never-ending love.
 I will survive the devil's fiery darts;
 and it's all because of Jesus' loving heart.
  Oh yes I am . . .

440
Anon
Copyright control

1. **Old man Noah built an ark—**
 hammer, hammer, bang, bang, ow!
 And that old ark was built of wood—
 hammer, hammer, bang, bang, ow!
 With a saw, saw, here and a nail, nail, there;
 here a nail, there a saw,
 everywhere a nail, nail;
 Old man Noah built an ark—
 hammer, hammer, bang, bang, ow!

2. The ark had a door without a knocker—
 hammer, hammer, bang, bang, ow!
 Everyone said, 'Noah's off his rocker'—
 hammer, hammer, bang, bang, ow!

With a 'ha ha' here, and a 'ho ho' there,
here a 'ha', there a 'ho',
everywhere a 'ha ha';
saw, saw here . . .

3. God shut the door and sent the rain—
pitter patter, pitter patter, splosh!
But all the people cried in vain—
pitter patter, pitter patter, splosh!
With a wail, wail here, and a shout, shout
   there,
here a shout, there a wail,
everywhere a shout, shout;
flush, flush here . . .
'ha ha' here . . .
saw, saw here . . .

4. For forty days they were afloat—
pitter patter, pitter patter, splosh!
But they were safe inside God's boat—
pitter patter, pitter patter, splosh!
So trust God here, believe God there,
here believe, there trust,
everywhere believe God;
wail, wail here . . .
flush, flush here . . .
'ha ha' here . . .
saw, saw here . . .

441 Traditional

1. **On Christmas night all Christians sing**
to hear the news the angels bring:
on Christmas night all Christians sing
to hear the news the angels bring:
news of great joy, news of great mirth,
news of our merciful King's birth.

2. Then why should we on earth be so sad,
since our Redeemer made us glad?
Then why should we on earth be so sad,
since our Redeemer made us glad;
when from our sin He set us free,
all for to gain our liberty?

3. When sin departs before His grace,
then life and death come in its place;
When sin departs before His grace,
then life and death come in its place;
angels and men with joy may sing,
all for to see the new-born King.

4. All out of darkness we have light,
which made the angels sing this night:
all out of darkness we have light,
which made the angels sing this night:
'Glory to God and peace to men,
now and for evermore. Amen.'

442 Anthony Welsh
© 1986 Kevin Mayhew Ltd

1. **On the road to Damascus**
the Lord appeared as a man was riding by:
his name was Saul.
I saw him fall
at a blinding flash from the sky.

'Saul! Saul! Do not persecute Me!
Saul! Saul! Do not persecute Me!'

2. On the road to Damascus
the Lord cried out to the man who could not
   see.
I heard Him call,
'Now tell Me, Saul,
just why do you persecute Me?'

'Saul! Saul! Do not persecute Me!
Saul! Saul! Do not persecute Me!'

3. On the road to Damascus
the Lord's voice came to the man whose eyes
   were blind.
I heard Him call
'Now hear Me, Saul,
I will change your name and your mind.'

Saul! Saul! Do not persecute Me!
Saul! Saul! Do not persecute Me!'

4. On the road to Damascus
I saw him fall to his knees before the Lord.
I heard Him call,
'Your name is Paul,
you must go out and spread My Word!'

'Paul! Paul! Teach the world of Jesus!
Paul! Paul! Teach the world of Jesus!'

5. On the road to Damascus
yes, I was there when the Lord's great power
   He showed.
I watched as Paul
received God's call
and then on my back he rode!

'Paul! Paul! Teach the world of Jesus!
Paul! Paul! Teach the world of Jesus!'

443 © 1988 Andy Silver

1. **Once upon a time it was many years ago**
Jesus told a story of a man that you should
   know.
He grew up on a farm and he had a hundred
   sheep;
the sheep would eat and eat and eat and eat.

'You're the sheep,' Jesus said,
'far from home, all alone.
I have come, God's own Son,
to find you and to bring you back to Him.'

2. When the sun went down he would lead them
   safely home;
   one and two and three and four, he'd count
   them on his own.
   Then one night he had a fright—he counted
   ninety nine;
   ninety, ninety, ninety, ninety nine.
   'You're the sheep . . .

3. Out he went to find where the missing sheep
   had strayed;
   searching high and low, he was feeling quite
   dismayed.
   Then he thought he heard a noise, it sounded
   like a bleat—
   he'd found the silly, sad and sorry sheep.
   'You're the sheep . . .

444

Ian White
© Little Misty Music Ltd

1. **Once there was a house, a busy little
   house,**
   and this is all about the busy little house.

2. Jesus Christ had come, teaching everyone;
   so everyone had to run to the busy little
   house.

3. Everyone was there, you couldn't find a chair;
   in fact you had to fight for air, in the busy little
   house.

4. A man who couldn't walk, was carried to the
   spot;
   but the place was chock-a-block, in the busy
   little house.

5. Whatever shall we do, whatever shall we do?
   We'll never get him through into the busy little
   house.

6. We'll open up the roof, we'll open up the roof;
   and then we'll put him through into the busy
   little house.

7. Then Jesus turned His eyes, and saw to His
   surprise,
   the man coming from the skies into the busy
   little house.

8. Then Jesus turned and said, 'Get up and take
   your bed,
   and run along instead from the busy little
   house'.

445

© 1991 Greg Leavers

One and two and three and four,
counting sheep in through the door;
fifty one and fifty two—
one is lost, what shall I do?

Ninety eight and ninety nine.
I will search until I find.
I will keep on looking just because I care.
There he is caught in some thorns way over
   there,
he was lost but now is found.
So it's ninety eight, ninety nine, (*click fingers*)
   one hundred;
yes it's ninety eight, ninety nine, (*click
   fingers*) one hundred!

446

Ian Smale
© 1982 Glorie Music/Thankyou Music

1. **Praise Him, praise Him,**
   bring praises to the Lord our God.
   All God's faithful children
   must learn to praise Him.
   Praise Him, praise Him,
   bring praises to the Lord our God.
   All God's faithful children
   must learn to praise Him.

   Sing hallelu, hallelu,
   sing hallelujah to our God.
   All God's faithful children
   sing hallelujah God.
   Sing hallelu, hallelu,
   sing hallelujah to our God.
   All God's faithful children
   sing hallelujah God.

2. Worship Him, worship Him,
   bring worship to the Lord our God.
   All God's faithful children
   must learn to worship Him.
   Worship Him, worship Him,
   bring worship to the Lord our God.
   All God's faithful children
   must learn to worship Him.
   Sing hallelu . . .

447

Anon
Copyright control

**Praise and thanksgiving let everyone
   bring,**
unto our Father for every good thing!
All together joyfully sing!

448

Paul Crouch and David Mudie
© 1991 Daybreak Music Ltd

Prayer is like a telephone
for us to talk to Jesus.
Prayer is like a telephone
for us to talk to God.
Prayer is like a telephone
for us to talk to Jesus.
Pick it up and use it every day.

We can shout out loud,
we can whisper softly,
we can make no noise at all;
but He'll always hear our call.

...... is like a telephone
for us to talk to Jesus.
...... is like a telephone
for us to talk to God.
...... is like a telephone
for us to talk to Jesus.
Pick it up and use it every day.

We can . . .

...... is like a ....
for us to talk to Jesus.
...... is like a ....
for us to talk to God.
...... is like a ....
for us to talk to Jesus.
Pick it up and use it every day.

We can . . .

...... is like a ....
for us to talk to .....
...... is like a ....
for us to talk to ...
...... is like a ....
for us to talk to .....
Pick it up and use it every day.
Pick it up and use it every day.
Pick it up and use it every day.

449
Ian White
© Little Misty Music Ltd

Roll the stone, roll the stone,
roll the stone away.
Jesus died, but He's alive,
and this is Easter day.

1. We all like to paint our eggs,
   sometimes blue and sometimes red.
   First we roll them till they crunch,
   then we eat them,
   (*spoken*) munch, munch, munch!
     Roll the stone . . .

2. We have chocolate eggs to eat,
   and inside there's lots of sweets.
   First they open with a crunch,
   then we eat them.
   (*spoken*) munch, munch, munch!
     Roll the stone . . .

450
© 1992 Gillian E. Hutchinson

1. **Saul had made himself a number of enemies,**
   who were busy plotting his death.

But his friends had no desire to discover him
suffering from shortage of breath.
To avoid a tragedy, they removed him
   secretly,
demonstrating brotherly love.
From enforced captivity, carefully they set
   him free,
demonstrating brotherly love.

2. Following the Lord can sometimes be difficult
   if we try to do it alone.
   We all need each other's help and
      encouragement
   as we learn to live as He's shown;
   serving others joyfully, showing generosity,
   demonstrating brotherly love;
   living in humility, bearing burdens patiently,
   demonstrating brotherly love.

3. All of us have different gifts, and abilities,
   which we need to learn how to share.
   We can all take part in building the fellowship
   showing the world we care;
   always speaking truthfully, harbouring no
      enmity,
   demonstrating brotherly love;
   working for Him faithfully, joined in perfect
      unity,
   demonstrating brotherly love.

451
Ian White
© Little Misty Music Ltd

1. **See the man walking, see the man walking,**
   see the man walking on the water.

   BOYS *This is a miracle,*
   GIRLS *His name is Jesus.*
   BOYS *How does He do it?*
   GIRLS *He is the Son of God.*
   BOYS *Can I believe Him?*
   GIRLS *You can believe Him.*
   BOYS *Really believe Him?*
   GIRLS *Really believe Him.*

2. Hear the man talking, hear the man talking,
   hear the man talking words of wisdom.
     This is a miracle . . .

3. See the man healing, see the man healing,
   see the man healing people blind and lame.
     This is a miracle . . .

4. See the man dying, see the man dying,
   see the man dying and come back to life.
     This is a miracle . . .

5. Hear the man promise, hear the man promise,
   hear the man promise to be with me.
     This is a miracle . . .

452 © Timothy Dudley-Smith

1. See, to us a Child is born—
   Glory breaks on Christmas morn!
   Now to us a Son is given—
   Praise to God in highest heaven.

2. On His shoulder rule shall rest—
   in Him all the earth be blest!
   Wise and wonderful His name—
   heaven's Lord in human frame!

3. Mighty God, who mercy brings—
   Lord of lords and King of kings!
   Father of eternal days—
   every creature sing His praise!

4. Everlasting Prince of peace—
   truth and righteousness increase!
   He shall reign from shore to shore—
   Christ is king for evermore!

453 © 1992 Steve Kersyss

Shine bright, dazzle, dazzle, shine bright,
   dazzle, dazzle.
The light of Jesus is shining bright;
shine bright, dazzle, dazzle, shine bright,
   dazzle, dazzle.
The light of Jesus is shining bright.
His life of love;
His life of light;
shines clear and bright in the darkest night.

454 © Timothy Dudley-Smith

1. Sing a new song to the Lord,
   He to whom wonders belong!
   Rejoice in His triumph and tell of His power—
   O sing to the Lord a new song!

2. Now to the ends of the earth,
   see His salvation is shown:
   and still He remembers His mercy and truth,
   unchanging in love to His own.

3. Sing a new song and rejoice,
   publish His praises abroad!
   Let voices in chorus, with trumpet and horn,
   resound for the joy of the Lord!

4. Join with the hills and the sea,
   thunders of praise to prolong!
   In judgement and justice He comes to the
      earth—
   O sing to the Lord a new song!

455 Derek Llewellyn
© 1991 Sea Dream Music

1. Sing praise to God the Father,
   God the Spirit, God the Son.
   Sing praise to God who loves us.
   Praise Him everyone!

2. Sing praise to God the Father,
   clap your hands and jump for joy.
   He made the world around us
   and He loves us all.

3. Sing praise to God's Son Jesus,
   clap your hands and jump for joy.
   Wave your arms and turn around.
   He teaches us about the Father
   and He loves us all.

4. Sing praise to the Holy Spirit,
   clap your hands and jump for joy.
   Wave your arms and jump around,
   stamp your feet and shout hooray.
   He helps us to live like Jesus
   and He loves us all.

5. Sing praise to God the Father,
   God the Spirit, God the Son:
   Sing praise to God who loves us.
   Praise Him everyone!

456 © 1991 Greg Leavers

Sing and celebrate (sing and celebrate);
God gave Jesus, (God gave Jesus);
Light for all the world (Light for all the world);
born at Christmas (born at Christmas time).

1. Jesus, our light,
   shines bright,
   what delight;
   came to reach us,
   teach us,
   lead us;
      Sing and celebrate . . .

2. God so loved us,
   gave us
   Jesus;
   Lord we thank You,
   love You,
   serve You;
      Sing and celebrate . . .

      Jesus, Light of the world,
      God's great gift of love.

457

Sing and celebrate (sing and celebrate);
Christ is risen (Christ is risen);
*Champion of the world (Champion of the
    world);*
    lives for ever (lives for evermore).

1. God so loved us,
   gave us
   Jesus;
   died on Calvary,
   set free
   you and me;
   Sing and celebrate . . .

2. Jesus our friend,
   died then
   rose again;
   Lord we love You,
   thank You,
   praise You;
   Sing and celebrate . . .

   Jesus died for the world,
   God's great gift of love.

458

1. **Six hundred years old was the preacher
   Noah**
   when the Lord said to build a boat;
   said a flood would come and cover the earth,
   and only Noah would stay afloat.
   Though the people laughed and called him
       names,
   he stayed right with his job.
   When he felt those drops, he knew his God
   had everything under control.

   He's got everything under control,
   He's got everything under control.
   The stars and the planets are in His hand,
   the wind and the rain at His command.
   You and I, we're a part of His plan;
   He's got everything under control.

2. Now Jonah had a whale of a problem
   when he turned that revival down.
   God tracked him down and boxed him in
   'cause he wouldn't go to that town.
   When He tells you to do what He wants you to
       do,
   don't think you can let it roll,
   'cause the God who made this universe
   has everything under control.
   He's got everything . . .

3. King Nebuchadnezzar lost his religion
   when the Hebrews wouldn't bow down.
   He lost his cool, fired up the furnace,

called a holiday in the town.
When he opened the door and threw them in,
they smiled at the burning coals,
'cause the God that allowed that fire to burn
had everything under control.
   He's got everything . . .

4. Daniel was invited to be on the menu
   at the meeting of the Lions' club,
   'cause he continued to pray three times a day
   to the Lord he had learned to love.
   When they threw him in he began to grin,
   'cause he knew what we all know;
   that the God who made those lions growl
   had everything under control.
   He's got everything . . .

459

So we're marching along,
singing a song, we're in the Lord's army.
We're fighting for right as we're learning
    what's wrong,
'cause we're in the Lord's army.
He's got the victory, so let's really shout,
we're in the Lord's army.
We're in the Lord's (*yeah*) we're in the Lord's
    (*right*),
we're in the Lord's army.
So we're marching along . . .

460

1. **Sometimes I'm naughty,**
   I know I've been bad;
   I say such unkind things
   and make people sad.

   Father, I know I've done wrong;
   Lord, please forgive me, I pray.
   I want to say,
   I want to say
   that I'm sorry, Lord.

2. I'm rude to my family,
   I want my own way.
   I don't show them kindness
   or do what they say.
      Father, I know . . .

3. In love You forgive me,
   I'm glad I'm Your child.
   Your Spirit lives in me
   to change me inside.

   Father help me today;
   Help me to please You, I pray.
   I want to say,
   I want to say
   how much I love You, Lord.

461

1. **Sometimes problems can be BIG,**
   sometimes problems can be *small*;
   but it doesn't really matter
   for whatever the size,
   Jesus wants to help us with them all
   so we can tell Him all about it.
   Trust His Word don't doubt it.
   Don't be afraid:
   DON'T BE AFRAID,
   just (1-2-3-4) believe.

2. Some days I wake up feeling GLAD,
   some days I wake up feeling *sad*;
   but it doesn't really matter
   for whatever the day
   Jesus wants to help us through them all.
   He's promised He will never leave us;
   He will not forsake us;
   don't be dismayed,
   DON'T BE AFRAID,
   just (1-2-3-4) believe.

462

1. **Some people laugh, some people sing,**
   some people clap; and so they bring
   their worship to the King of kings.
   What do you do? What do you do?

2. Some people dance, some bring a word,
   some people cry before the Lord;
   and so they bring their worship to
   the King of kings, the King of kings.

3. Some people march and raise their hands
   and some are quiet but understand.
   There are many ways of worshipping
   the King of kings, the King of kings.

463

1. **Sorry Lord, for all the things**
   that I've done wrong; please
   make me clean, forgive my sin—
   I want to follow You.

2. Thank You Lord, for dying on
   the cross to save me;
   fill my heart for my new start—
   please come and live in me.

3. I love You, please help me Lord
   to follow closely;
   from today, in every way
   please make me more like You.

464

1. **Spies were sent out to**
   view the promised land.
   Ten said, 'There are giants there:
   we can't do as we planned.'
   Joshua and Caleb said,
   'We must make a stand.'
   The Lord said, 'Follow Me,
   I'll place them in your hand.'

   We've got to hear, believe and obey,
   whatever the Father might say;
   for He is a good God and He only wants
   the best for us.

2. When Joshua saw the size of
   Jericho's great wall—
   towering high above him,
   many metres tall—
   though it looked impossible
   to take the town at all,
   the Lord said, 'Obey Me
   and down the walls will fall.'
   We've go to . . .

3. So when you're feeling scared or
   things are looking blue—
   you've got a job that seems so
   difficult to do—
   don't forget His promises
   He's made to help you through;
   the Lord says, 'Don't be afraid
   I'll always be with you.'
   We've got to . . .

465

Spirit of God, please fill me now to
   overflowing.
Spirit of God, give me the words You want me
   to say.
Spirit of God, release my tongue to praise the
   Holy Son;
Spirit of God, free this spirit of mine.

466

Standing in Your presence Lord,
we are here to praise Your name.
Standing in Your presence Lord,
Your great goodness we proclaim.

1. You alone are God the Lord,
   Master of the earth and sky.
   All the stars in heaven worship, and yet,
   when we call You Lord, You hear our cry.

Standing in Your presence Lord,
we will lift our hands to You.
Standing in Your presence Lord,
giving thanks for all You do.

2. You have brought us here today,
   kept and guided for so long.
   There's no need for tears or sadness,
   the joy that You give us, Lord, will make us
   strong.

   Standing in Your presence Lord,
   listening to Your holy law.
   Standing in Your presence Lord,
   we will praise You evermore.

467 © 1989 Andy Silver

**Thank you for the love that our mums give
   to us each day;**
   thank You for the help and the care that they
   bring our way.
   Lord, we thank You for everything they do,
   show us how to help them too.
   Show us how to live, teaching us to
   appreciate;
   show us how to live so that we don't infuriate.
   Lord, we ask that in everything they do,
   may our mums be blessed by You.

468 Valerie Collison
© 1970 Hye-Fye Music Ltd

1. **The journey of life may be easy, may be
   hard,**
   there'll be dangers on the way;
   with Christ at my side I'll do battle as I ride
   'gainst the foe that would lead me astray.

   Will you ride, ride, ride with the King of
   kings,
   will you follow my Leader true;
   will you shout hosanna to the holy Son of
   God,
   who died for me and you?

2. My burden is light and a song is in my heart,
   as I travel on life's way;
   for Christ is my Lord and He's given me His
   Word,
   that by my side He'll stay.
   Will you ride . . .

3. When doubts arise and when tears are in my
   eyes,
   when all seems lost to me;
   with Christ as my guide I can smile whate'er
   betide,
   for He my strength will be.
   Will you ride . . .

4. I'll follow my Leader wherever He may go,
   for Jesus is my Friend;
   He'll lead me on to the place where He has
   gone,
   when I come to my journey's end.
   Will you ride . . .

469 Paul Kenchington
© 1984 Kevin Mayhew Ltd

1. **The Lord is risen today!**
   The Lord is risen today!
   The Lord is risen today!
   The Lord is risen today!
   Alleluia! Alleluia! Alleluia!
   The Lord is risen today!

2. And we will sing His praise,
   and we will sing His praise,
   and we will sing His praise;
   the Lord is risen today!
   Alleluia! Alleluia! Alleluia!
   The Lord is risen today!

3. Oh, Jesus died for me!
   Yes, Jesus died for me!
   Yes, Jesus died for me,
   but the Lord is risen indeed!
   Alleluia! Alleluia! Alleluia!
   The Lord is risen today!

470 Ian Smale
© 1985 Glorie Music/Thankyou Music

**The most important thing for us as
   Christians**
   is not what we eat or drink,
   but stirring up goodness, peace and joy
   from the Holy Spirit.

471 Hilda Rostron
© National Christian Education Council

1. **The shepherds found the stable**
   and saw the Baby there;
   they quietly knelt beside Him
   and said a 'thank you' prayer.

2. The wise men found the Baby
   and gave gifts, one, two, three;
   today it is His birthday:
   my gift is—LOVE from me.

472 Damien Lundy
© Kevin Mayhew Ltd, licence no 191180

1. **The Spirit lives to set us free,**
   walk, walk in the light;
   He binds us all in unity,
   walk, walk in the light.

Walk in the light,
walk in the light,
walk in the light,
walk in the light of the Lord.

2. Jesus promised life to all,
   walk, walk in the light;
   the dead were wakened by His call,
   walk, walk in the light.
      Walk in the light . . .

3. He died in pain on Calvary,
   walk, walk in the light;
   to save the lost like you and me,
   walk, walk in the light.
      Walk in the light . . .

4. We know His death was not the end,
   walk, walk in the light;
   He gave His Spirit to be our friend,
   walk, walk in the light.
      Walk in the light . . .

5. By Jesus' life our wounds are healed,
   walk, walk in the light;
   the Father's kindness is revealed,
   walk, walk in the light.
      Walk in the light . . .

6. The Spirit lives in you and me,
   walk, walk in the light;
   His light will shine for all to see,
   walk, walk in the light.
      Walk in the light . . .

473
Alan J. Price
© 1990 Daybreak Music Ltd

The Word of the Lord is planted in my heart
and I want to see it grow.
The Word of the Lord is planted in my heart
and I want you to know.
I won't let the enemy take it,
or let bad times shake it;
I won't let other things choke it out (*choke*
   choke choke choke),
'cos I want to let it grow, grow, grow,
'cos I want to let it grow! (*last time*) (*Yeah!*)

474
Mick Gisbey
© 1985 Thankyou Music

The word of God is living and active,
sharper than any double-edged sword.
The Word of God is living and active,
sharper than any double-edged sword.

475
© 1992 Gillian E. Hutchinson

1. **There he stood, Goliath, mighty man in**
   armour bright;
   compared to him you'd not say David was
      prepared to fight.

When Goliath saw him, he could not believe
   his eyes;
before him stood a boy he did despise.
'Do you think I am a dog, to fight me with a
   stick?
I'll throw your flesh to animals, your bones for
   birds to pick!'
Shouting murderous curses, he cried out,
   'Prepare to die!'
But David spoke up boldly in reply.

'Not with spear, not with sword
but in the name of the Lord;
in the name of the One you have defied.
He's victorious in battle,
He will save us by His power;
strength and deliverance He'll provide;
I'm fighting on the Lord Almighty's side!'

2. Moving closer in, Goliath started his attack
   but David ran to meet him—he did not turn
      and run back.
   With his sling he threw a stone which to
      Goliath sped;
   it broke his skull and sank into his head!
   The giant had been conquered—he fell down
      upon the floor—
   then David chopped his head off and Goliath
      was no more!
   All of Israel's army knew the mighty deed was
      done
   and in whose name the victory had been won.
      'Not with spear . . .

3. Life is filled with problems which may give us
      cause to fear.
   But though they seem like giants, just
      remember God is near.
   He will always help us when we put our trust
      in Him.
   In the name of Jesus we shall win.
      'Not with spear . . .

476
Paul Field
© 1991 Daybreak Music Ltd

There is no-one else like you,
there's no-one else like me.
Each of us is special to God,
that's the way it's meant to be.
I'm special, you're special,
we're special don't you see?
There is no-one else like you,
there's no-one else like me.

Black or white, short or tall,
good or bad, God loves us all.
Loud or quiet, fat or thin,
each of us is special to Him.

There is no-one . . .

477
Anon
Copyright control

There once was a man called Daniel
(*good old Daniel*).
And Daniel prayed three times a day
(*good old Daniel*).
but the King's decree said 'Worship me!'
(*poor old Daniel*).
But Daniel would not bend the knee!
(*good old Daniel*).
So the gates went 'crash' (*crash*),
and the locks went 'click' (*click*),
and the lions began to roar,
and the lions began to roar.
But they couldn't eat Daniel if they tried
(*good old Daniel*).
because the Lord was on his side.
(*good old Daniel*).

478
Albert Midlane (1825–1909)
© in this version Jubilate Hymns

1. **There's a song for all the children**
   that makes the heavens ring,
   a song that even angels
   can never never sing;
   they praise Him as their Maker
   and see Him glorified,
   but we can call Him Saviour
   because for us He died.

2. There's a place for all the children
   where Jesus reigns in love,
   a place of joy and freedom
   that nothing can remove;
   a home that is more friendly
   than any home we know,
   where Jesus makes us welcome
   because He loves us so.

3. There's a friend for all the children
   to guide us every day,
   whose care is always faithful
   and never fades away;
   there's no-one else so loyal—
   His friendship stays the same;
   He knows us and He loves us,
   and Jesus is His name.

479
Susan Sayers
© 1986 Kevin Mayhew Ltd, licence no 191180

1. **Think big: an elephant.**
   Think bigger: a submarine.
   Think bigger: the highest mountain that
       anyone has ever seen.
   Yet, big, big, bigger is God!
   And He loves us all.

2. Think old: a vintage car.
   Think older: a full-grown tree.
   Think older: a million grains of the sand
       beside the surging sea.
   Yet old, old, older is God!
   And He loves us all.

3. Think strong: a tiger's jaw.
   Think stronger: a castle wall.
   Think stronger: a hurricane that leaves little
       standing there at all.
   Yet strong, strong, stronger is God!
   And He loves us all.

480
Graham Kendrick
© Make Way Music/Thankyou Music

1. **This Child, secretly comes in the night;**
   oh, this Child, hiding a heavenly light;
   oh, this Child, coming to us like a stranger;
   this heavenly Child.

   This Child, heaven come down now to be with
       us here;
   heavenly love and mercy appear;
   softly in awe and wonder come near
   to this heavenly Child.

2. This Child, rising on us like the sun;
   oh this Child, giving to light everyone;
   oh this Child, guiding our feet on the pathway
   to peace on earth.
       This Child, heaven come down . . .

3. This Child, raising the humble and poor;
   oh this Child, making the proud ones to fall;
   this Child, filling the hungry with good things;
   this heavenly Child.
       This Child, heaven come down . . .
       This Child, heaven come down . . .

481
Alan J. Price
© 1990 Daybreak Music Ltd

This is a catchy songa,
we sing it to the Conga,
we dance and sing
to Christ the King.
Why don't you sing alonga,
while we dance the Conga?
Praise God above for all His love!

1. King David danced before the Lord,
   worship filled his heart;
   we can dance before Him, too,
   this is how we start.
       This is a catchy songa . . .

2. Jesus is the greatest Friend
   alive for us today,
   He said, 'I'm with you till the end,
   I'm with you all the way.'
       This is a catchy songa . . .

482 © 1985 Andy Silver

**Wandering like lost sheep we were going
    our own way,**
when Jesus the good Shepherd found us, led
    us home,
laid down His life before us that we might all
    be saved.
We now belong to Jesus, we now belong to
    Him.
We are His sheep, we are His sheep,
we hear His voice, and follow Him.
We are His sheep, we are His sheep,
we hear His voice and follow Him.

483 © 1990 Greg Leavers

We are soldiers of the King,
of His victory we will sing;
living every hour by the Spirit's power,
marching in the name of Jesus.
Enemies are all around,
as we praise they're losing ground;
trusting in God's Word—it's a mighty sword—
forever friendly, faithful followers fighting for
    the King.

484 Alan J. Price
© 1990 Daybreak Music Ltd

We need to grow, grow, grow, grow,
grow in the grace of the Saviour.
We need to grow, grow, grow, grow,
grow in the knowledge of Jesus our Lord.
We need to grow, grow, grow, grow,
grow in the grace of the Saviour.
We need to grow, grow, grow, grow,
grow in the knowledge of Jesus our Lord.

1. We'll grow as we pray to Him,
    spend some time each day.
    We'll grow as we worship Him,
    give Him our love and praise!

    We need to grow, grow, grow, grow,
    grow in the grace of the Saviour.
    We need to grow, grow, grow, grow,
    grow in the knowledge of Jesus our Lord.

2. We grow as we read of Him and the
    way for us to live;
    we'll grow as we work for Him,
    as our lives to Him we give.
      We need to grow . . .

3. We grow as we learn and share
    with others that we know;
    these are the things to do
    if we really want to grow.

    We need to grow . . .
    grow in the knowledge of,
    grow in the knowledge of Jesus our Lord.

485 Ian Smale
© 1984 Glorie Music/Thankyou Music

**We will praise, we will praise, we will
    praise the Lord;**
we will praise the Lord because He is good.
We will praise, we will praise, we will praise
    the Lord,
because His love is everlasting.
We will praise, we will praise, we will praise
    the Lord;
we will praise the Lord because He is good.
We will praise, we will praise, we will praise
    the Lord,
because His love is everlasting.

Bring on the trumpets and harps,
let's hear the cymbals ring;
then in harmony,
lift our voices and sing, sing.

We will praise, we will praise, we will praise
    the Lord;
we will praise the Lord because He is good.
We will praise, we will praise, we will praise
    the Lord,
because His love is everlasting.

486 Ian Smale
© 1984 Glorie Music/Thankyou Music

1. **We'll praise Him on the trumpet and we'll
    praise Him on guitar,**
    we'll praise Him with a drum and with a harp
        and a lyre.
    We'll praise Him with our voices 'cause we
        want to lift Him higher;
    and all God's people shout 'Hallelujah!'

    Hallelujah, hallelujah, hallelujah, hallelujah.
    Hallelujah, hallelujah, and all God's people
        shout 'Hallelujah!'

2. We'll praise Him for His favour and we'll
        praise Him for His deeds;
    we'll praise Him—though the road is rough,
        He's still the one who leads.
    We'll praise Him for provision as He cares for
        all our needs,
    and all God's people shout 'Hallelujah!'
      Hallelujah, hallelujah . . .

3. We'll praise Him that upon a cross the Lamb
        of God was slain;
    we'll praise Him that He conquered death
        and now He lives again.
    We'll praise Him—He's the King of kings who
        will forever reign,
    and all God's people shout 'Hallelujah!'
      Hallelujah, hallelujah . . .

4. We'll praise Him that He's making us the
     people we should be;
   we'll praise Him that our chains are gone,
     we're now completely free.
   We'll praise Him—we don't know defeat, we
     live in victory,
   and all God's people shout 'Hallelujah!'
     Hallelujah, hallelujah . . .

487 Robert C. Evans
        © 1990 Integrity's Hosanna! Music

We're following Jesus,
just like Matthew, Peter and John.
We're following Jesus,
just like Thaddeus, Philip and Tom.
We're following Jesus,
just like Simon, James and Andrew.
Like them, the Lord is calling me and you.

1. They all loved Him (*I want to love Him*),
   they all served Him (*I want to serve Him*).
   They all knew Him (*I want to know Him*),
   they all followed (*I want to follow*).
     We're following . . .

2. Jesus taught them (*Teach me, Lord*),
   Jesus led them (*Lead me, Lord*).
   Jesus fed them (*Feed me, Lord*),
   Jesus used them (*Use me, Lord*).
     We're following . . .

488 © Timothy Dudley-Smith

1. **What colours God has made**
   in flower and field and tree!
   From springing green of leaf and blade
   I learn His love for me.

2. The summer's yellow sand,
   the blue of sky and sea,
   they tell of God their Maker's hand,
   and all His love for me.

3. The turning autumn leaves,
   the fruit so full and free,
   the golden glow of harvest sheaves,
   declare His love for me.

4. He frames the winter's skies,
   His silver stars I see;
   He makes the sun in splendour rise,
   the God who cares for me.

5. So sing my Father's praise,
   the living God is He,
   whose colours brighten all our days,
   who loves and cares for me.

489 Nancy Harrison
        © Lillenas Publishing Co/Thankyou Music

1. **What do you give a God who has
     everything?**
   What do you give a God who has it all?
   He is the One who flung the shining galaxies
     in space!
   He is the One who hung the stars in place!

2. What do you give a God who has everything?
   What do you give the Maker of the earth?
   Give Him your life and let Him guide you;
   trust Him in all your ways!
   Give Him your heart; He'll fill it up with praise!
   Give Him your heart; He'll fill it up with praise!

490 W. J. and Gloria Gaither
        © 1975 Gaither Music Co/United Nations Publishing
        Ltd/Boosey & Hawkes Music Publishers Ltd

1. **What drives the stars without making a
     sound?**
   Why don't they crash when they're spinning
     around?
   What holds me up when the world's upside
     down?
   I know it's a miracle!
   Who tells the ocean where to stop on the
     sand?
   What keeps the water back from drowning the
     land?
   Who makes the rules I don't understand?
   I know it's a miracle!

   It's a miracle just to know
   God is with me wherever I go.
   It's a miracle as big as can be,
   that He can make a miracle of me!

2. Who shows the birds how to make a good
     nest?
   How can the geese fly so far without rest?
   Why do the ducks go south and not west?
   I know it's a miracle!
   What makes a brown seed so tiny and dry
   burst into green and grow up so high?
   And shoot out blossoms of red by and by?
   I know it's a miracle!
     It's a miracle . . .

3. When a spring makes a brook and a brook
     makes a stream,
   the stream makes the river water fresh as can
     be.
   Who puts the salt in when it gets to the sea?
   I know it's a miracle!
   There are thousands of people in cities I see,
   the world must be crowded as crowded can
     be;
   but God knows my name and He cares about
     me.
   I know it's a miracle!

491

Anon
Copyright control

1. **What a mighty God we serve . . .**
   (*4 times*)

2. He created you and me . . .

3. He has all the power to save . . .

4. Let us praise the living God . . .

5. What a mighty God we serve . . .

492

© 1992 Gillian E. Hutchinson

1. **What made a difference in the life of Saul,**
   to change him from a sinner to Apostle Paul?
   He met Jesus and suddenly knew
   that all he'd hated turned out to be true.
   Instead of persecuting those who followed
     His name,
   he started in the synagogue His love to
     proclaim.
   Yes, who'd have thought that Saul could be
     transformed
   into the greatest missionary.

2. On several journeys the apostle was sent,
   and suffered many difficulties as he went.
   Beaten, shipwrecked, imprisoned was he
   but learnt to glory in adversity.
   The churches grew and flourished and the
     Gospel was spread,
   and many found salvation through the things
     that he said.
   Yes, who'd have thought that Saul could be
   transformed into the greatest missionary.

3. He wrote some letters to the churches he
     knew,
   to Ephesus, Colossi and Galatia too.
   To Philippi and Corinth he wrote,
   to Rome and Thessalonica, epistles of note.
   Timothy and Titus and Philemon all heard
   and what he wrote has now become a part of
     God's Word.
   Yes, who'd have thought that Saul could be
   transformed into the greatest missionary.

4. If you've decided that your life must change,
   then give it to the Lord for Him to rearrange.
   He will be your Saviour and Friend,
   and on His presence you can depend.
   You may not be a missionary or travel around,
   but all of us can witness to the joy that we've
     found.
   Yes, what the Lord could do for Saul,
   He's ready now to do for one and all!

493

© 1991 Greg Leavers

**When I'm feeling lonely, when I'm feeling
  blue,**
when I'm feeling so fed up, I can always talk
  to You.
Lord, You hear me when I pray;
Lord, You're near me every day.
Thank You Lord, You always see me through;
I'll never, ever, find a friend as good as You.
I'll never, ever, find a friend as good as You.

494

Paul Field and Ralph Chambers
© 1991 Daybreak Music Ltd

When the dark clouds are above you,
there's no sunshine anywhere;
when you feel that no one loves you,
when you feel that no one cares;
talk to the Saviour,
He knows how you feel.
His love lasts forever,
His love for you is real.
Talk to the Saviour,
no matter what you do.
You've got a friend in Jesus,
He always loves you.

When the dark . . .

495

© 1988 Andy Silver

When we look up to the sky
and we see the sparrows fly,
let's remember that Jesus knows them all.
When we see the lovely trees
and the flowers and the leaves,
let's remember that Jesus made them all.
J.E.S.U.S. C.A.R.E.S.
Jesus cares for all the things He made:
that means you and me,
our friends and family.
Thank You Jesus for caring for me.

496

Paul Field and Ralph Chambers
© 1991 Daybreak Music Ltd

**When you're feeling good put your thumbs
  up.**
When you're feeling bad put them down.
When you're feeling happy you can smile all
  day.
When you're feeling low wear a frown.
But don't just follow your feelings.
Trust in God and His Word.
No matter what you feel put your thumbs up,
put your faith in the Lord.

497

When God breathes His Spirit in my life;
when God breathes His Spirit in my life;
When God breathes His Spirit in my life,
then I will shine shine for Him.

498

1. **Would you walk by on the other side**
   when someone called for aid?
   Would you walk by on the other side,
   and would you be afraid?

   Cross over the road my friend;
   ask the Lord His strength to lend;
   His compassion has no end.
   Cross over the road.

2. Would you walk by on the other side
   when you saw a loved one stray?
   Would you walk by on the other side,
   or would you watch and pray?
     Cross over the road . . .

3. Would you walk by on the other side
   when starving children cried?
   Would you walk by on the other side,
   and would you not provide?

   Cross over the road my friend;
   ask the Lord His strength to lend;
   His compassion has no end.
   Cross over the road,
   cross over the road,
   cross over the road.

499

Yet to all who received Him,
to those who believed in His name,
He gave the right to become the children of
   God.
Yet to all who received Him,
to those who believed in His name,
He gave the right to become the children of
   God.

500

You are holy, so You hate all we do wrong.
You are loving, for our sin You gave Your Son.
You are Father, the great protector;
You are mighty, the great Creator;
You are faithful, You are wonderful,
You are King and You are God.

501

1. **You can weigh an elephant's auntie,**
   you can weigh a pedigree flea;
   but you can't weight up all the love
   that Jesus has for me, me, me,
   that Jesus has for me.

2. You can measure the length of a wiggly
      worm,
   or the height of a nanny goat's knee;
   but you can't measure all the love
   that Jesus has for me, me, me,
   that Jesus has for me.

3. You can add up two and two, make four,
   it's as easy as A, B, C;
   but you can't add up all the love
   that Jesus has for me, me, me,
   that Jesus has for me.

4 You can amaze me by subtraction,
   you can even take three from three;
   but you can't take away the love
   that Jesus has for me, me, me,
   that Jesus has for me.

502

You can't catch a plane to take you to
   heaven.
Not even a spaceship can get that far.
You can't take a hover-craft or helicopter
   journey
or drive in the fastest racing car.
Only Jesus, only Jesus, only Jesus is the
   way.
Only Jesus, only Jesus, only Jesus is the
   way.

503

You're my Maker, You're my music,
You're the Master of my life.
You're my Maker, You're my music,
You're the Master of my life.
You're my Maker, You're my music,
You're the Master of my life,
and I love You, Jesus my Lord.

Copyright Addresses

C M Alexander's Copyright Trust, S W Grant 12 Lawrie Park Crescent, Sydenham, London SE26 6HD

G F Allen Barton Cottage, Station Road, Blockley, Glos. GL56 5OT

John Arlott, PO Box 34, The Vines, Longis Road, Alderney CI

Cliff Barrows, Melody Lane, Rt. 9 No Parker Road, Greenville, South Carolina 29609 USA

Benson Co Inc/Boosey & Hawkes

A & C Black (Publishers) Ltd, Howard Road, Eaton Socon, Huntingdon, Cambs. PE19 3EZF

Fred Bock Music/Thankyou Music

Boosey & Hawkes Music Publishers Ltd, 295 Regent Street, London, WR1 8JH

J A P Booth, 187 Walmsworth Road, Doncaster, S Yorks DN4 OTW

Bosworth & Co Ltd, 14/18 Heddon Street, London W1R 8DP

Laura Bradley c/o HarperCollins Religious

Gordon Brattle, N A M Cooke, 52 Birch Grove, Ealing Common, London W3 9SR

Breitkopf & Hartel, Walkmuhl, D-6200, Wiesbaden 1, Germany

Allen Brown c/o HarperCollins Religious

Phil Burt, 5 Gardner Road, Warton, Nr Carnforth, Lancashire LA5 9NY

Annie Bush c/o HarperCollins Religious

BMG Music Publishing, 8370 Wilshire Boulevard, Beverly Hills, California 90211, USA, USA

J H Cansdale, 12 Belfield Close, Weymouth, Dorset, DT4 9RG

Celebration/Thankyou Music

Chappell Music Ltd, 129 Park Street, London W1

Child Evangelism Fellowship Inc, Box 348, Warrenton, MO 63383 USA

Christian Music Ministries, 325 Bromfield Road, Hodge Hill, Birmingham, B36 8ET

Church Hymnal Foundation, USA

Norman J Clayton Publishing/Word Music

Cliff College, Ridgeway, Cliff Lane, Curbas, Sheffield S30 1XD

Douglas Coombes, Lindsay Music Entertainments, 23 Hitchin Street, Biggleswade, Beds. SG18 8AX

Daybreak Music Ltd, 4 Regency Mews, Silverdale Road, Eastbourne, East Sussex BN20 7AB

Paul S Deming, 8987 St Louis Avenue, St Louis, Miss. 63114 USA

S & J Doddridge, c/o HarperCollins Religious

Timothy Dudley-Smith, 9 Ashlands, Ford, Salisbury, Wilts SP4 6DY

William Elkin Music Services, Station Road Industrial Estate, Salhouse, Norwich, Norfolk

E M I Publishing, 127 Charing Cross Road, London WC2H OLD

Franciscan Communications, 1229 South Santee Street, Los Angeles, California 90015 USA

Roland Fudge, High Grain, Austwick, Lancaster LA2 8AW

Gaither Music, Boosey & Hawkes

Doris M Gill, Kerry Hill, Hawling, Andoversford, Glos. GL54 5SZ

Glorie Music/Thankyou Music

Exec Bareham Gould, D R Gould, 34 Pollard Drive, Horsham, West Sussex

Archie Hall, Lochinver, 69 King George V Avenue, Kings Lynn, Norfolk PE30 2QE

Jeanne Harper, Stanfords, 27 Munster Green, Haywards Heath, West Sussex, RH16 4AL

HarperCollins*Religious*, 77–85 Fulham Palace Road, Hammersmith, London W6 8JB

Exec Basil Harwood, Public Trustee, Stewart House, Kingsway, London WC2B 6JX

Herald Music Service, 28 Church Circle, Farnborough, Hants

High-Fye Music, Campbell Connelly & Co Ltd, 8/9 Frith Street, London W1V 5TZ

David Higham Associates, 5–8 Lower John Street, Golden Square, London W1R 4HA

His Eye Music, BMG Music Publishers, 8370 Wilshire Boulevard, Beverly Hills, California 90211 USA

Ruth Hooke, 9 Cyprus Grove, Lostock Hall, Preston PR5 5BB

Hope Publishing Company, 380 S Main Place, Carol Stream, Illinois 60188 USA

Peter Horrobin, Ellel Grange, Ellel, Nr Lancaster LA2 OHN

Horrobin & Leavers c/o Peter Horrobin

Andy Hughes, 14 Mount Pleasant, Lindel in Furness, Cumbria LA12 OLZ

Roger Hurrell c/o HarperCollins Religious

Gillian E Hutchinson, 121 Glenwood Drive, Irby, Wirral, Merseyside, L61 4U7

Fiona Inkpen c/o HarperCollins Religious

Integrity Music UK Ltd, PO Box 101 Eastbourne, East Sussex BN21 3UX

Jubilate Hymns, Mrs B Grundy, 61 Chessel Avenue, Southampton SO2 4DY

Ron Jones, Maybank, 10 Croft Lane, Moor Park, Liverpool 9

Carolyn Keats, 12 Salisbury Drive, Swanage, Dorset BH19 2DY

B M Kerr, Wayside Cottage, East Dene, Eastbourne, East Sussex

Steve Kersyss, Oakshade, Peartree Farm, Bickenacre, Chelmsford, Essex CM3 4ES

Greg Leavers, 1 Haws Hill, Cove Road, Carnforth, Lancs

Leo Song Copyright Services, Westmead House, 123 Westmead Road, Sutton, Surrey SM1 4BJH

Peter Lewis, 22 Marlborough Rise, Aston, Sheffield S31 OET

Lexicon Music/Boosey & Hawkes

Little Misty Music Ltd, PO Box 8 Perth PH2 7EX

Lillenas Publishing House/Thankyou Music

Ludlow Music, TRO Essex Music Ltd, Suite 2.07 Plaza, 535 Kings Road, London SW10 052

Make Way Music Ltd, PO Box 683 Hailsham, East Sussex BN27 4ZB

Maranatha Music/Word Music

Kevin Mayhew Publishers, Rattlesden, Bury St Edmunds, Suffolk IP30 OSZ

Mercy Publishing/Thankyou Music

Roland Meredith, The Rectory, 13 Station Road, Witney, Oxon OX8 6BH

Moody Bible Institute, 820 North LaSalle Street, Chicago IL. 60610 USA

McCrimmon Publishing Company, 10–12 High Street, Great Wakering, Essex SS3 OEG

National Christian Education Council, Robert Denholm House, Nutfield, Redhill, Surrey RH1 4HW

New Jerusalem Music/Thankyou Music

Oaksprings Impressions, PO Box 394, Fairfax, CA 94930 USA

Oxford University Press, 3 Park Road, London NW1 6XN

Paget Publications, Rose Cottage, Ashcott, Bridgwater, Somerset

Joan Robinson, 47 Woodlands Road, Beaumont, Lancaster LA1 2EH

Rocksmith Music/Leo Song

Rodeheaver/Word Music (UK)

R Rusbridge, 9 Springfield House, Cotham Road, Bristol BS6 6DQ

Sacred Songs USA

Salvationist Publishing & Supplies Ltd, 117–121 Judd Street, King's Cross, London WC1H 9NN

S Lesley Scott c/o HarperCollins Religious

Scripture Gift Mission, Radstock House, 3 Eccleston Street, London SW1W 9LZ

Scripture Press Publications Inc, 1825 College Avenue, Wheaton, Ill 60187 USA

Scripture Union, 130 City Road, London EC1V 2NJ

Sea Dream Music, 236 Sabert Road, Forest Gate, London E7 ONP

Robin Sheldon, 56 Besselsleigh Road, Wooton, Oxford

Andy Silver, 24 Abbots Way, Portswood, Southampton, SO2 1NS

C Simmonds, School House, 81 Clapham Road, Bedford, MK41 7RB

Annie & Neil Simpson, 7 Mungosnelly Cottages, North Berwick, East Lothian EH39 5AT

Sparrow Song/BMG Music Publishing

Singspiration Inc/Boosey & Hawkes

Springtide/Word Music (UK)

Stainer & Bell Ltd, PO Box 110, Victoria House, 23 Gruneisen Road, London N3 1DZ

Thankyou Music PO Box 75, Eastbourne, East Sussex BN23 6NT

United Nations Music Publishing/Boosey & Hawkes

Waif/Heath Levy, c/o Paul Field, 26 Demesne Road, Wallington, Surrey SM6 8PP

Josef Weinberger Ltd, 12–14 Mortimer Street, London W1N 7RD

Margaret Westworth, 11a The Drive, Crag Bank, Carnforth, Lancs.

Word Music (UK) Ltd, 9 Holdom Avenue, Bletchley, Milton Keynes, MK1 1QR

Word of God Music Ltd, PO Box 8617, Ann Arbor, Michigan 48107 USA

Subject Index

Index of First Lines

Titles which differ from first lines are shown in bold